CW00410718

SCIENCE WITH PURPOSE:
Fifty years of the Institute of
Occupational Medicine

IOM

SCIENCE WITH PURPOSE:

Fifty years of the Institute of Occupational Medicine

Anthony Seaton (Editor) · Robert J Aitken
John W Cherrie · Richard A Graveling
Fintan Hurley · Alastair Robertson
Colin A Soutar · Philip J Woodhead

Institute of Occupational Medicine
49 Research Avenue North, Riccarton, Edinburgh, EH14 4AP,
Scotland, United Kingdom
www.iom-world.org

Matador
9 Priory Business Park,
Wistow Road, Kibworth Beauchamp,
Leicestershire, LE8 0RX
Tel: 0116 279 2299
Email: books@troubador.co.uk
Web: www.troubador.co.uk/matador
Twitter: @matadorbooks

ISBN 978 1838591 229

British Library Cataloguing in Publication Data.
A catalogue record for this book is available from the British Library.

Printed and bound by CPI Group (UK) Ltd, Croydon, CR0 4YY
Typeset in 9.5 Helvetica by Troubador Publishing Ltd, Leicester, UK

Matador is an imprint of Troubador Publishing Ltd

Anthony Seaton (Editor), IOM 1978-1990;
Director, 1978-1990

Robert J Aitken, IOM 1974-date;
Chief Executive, 2016-date

John W Cherrie, IOM 1975-date;
Research Director, 2007-14

Richard A Graveling, IOM 1978-date;
Head of Ergonomics and Human Factors, 1990-2014

Fintan Hurley, IOM 1975-2017;
Scientific Director, 2005-17

Alastair Robertson, IOM 1974-2013;
Managing Director Consultancy, 1997-2008

Colin A Soutar, IOM 1979-2005;
Chief Executive, 1990-2005

Philip J Woodhead, IOM 2005-16;
Chief Executive, 2005-16

To celebrate our 50th anniversary, IOM commissioned Innovation Digital, a Glasgow based design agency to create 50 pieces of unique, digital artwork. Each design focuses on one of the 50 most significant scientific impacts IOM has made over the last half-century. The images were exhibited at IOM's 50th Anniversary reception at the Scottish Parliament on 8th October 2019. Images on the cover of this book are a selection of the artwork appearing in the exhibition. The full collection can be viewed on the IOM Website.

Contents

Acknowledgements

This history of IOM provides a set of personal perspectives about the people and the major events that have shaped the organisation over the last fifty years. In writing this book, the authors, all of whom have served in senior positions in IOM, have drawn heavily on their personal recollections as well as those of some current and former colleagues. In particular, the authors would like to thank Professor Ken Donaldson and Drs Alan Jones, Joanne Crawford, Lang Tran, Rob Bolton, Geoff Simpson, Brian Miller, Hilary Cowie and Matt Boyles for their contributions and reflections. Thanks are also due to Ken Dixon, IOM's Information Scientist, for help with editing, information sourcing and referencing, Aimee Taaffe, IOM's Marketing Manager, for design elements and book production, and to Melanie Gee, Words and Indexes, for indexing.

The authors would like to thank the Mining Institute of Scotland Trust for their generous grant which supported book production and publication.

Finally and most importantly, thanks are due to all of IOM's staff who have contributed with their insight, knowledge, dedication and effort to the work of IOM throughout its history and to the current staff who are shaping its future. Over the last fifty years almost 1,000 people, too many to mention in this volume, have devoted a significant part of their working lives to creating a unique and special organisation which has made major contributions to improving health in the workplace and wider environment. This book is a tribute to them. Without their work, nothing would have been achieved.

Thanks to you all.

This book has been written in celebration of IOM's fifty-year anniversary. It is intended to preserve and highlight the exceptional work of those that have passed through the Institute's doors.

Introduction

Fifty years of the Institute of Occupational Medicine

In 2019, the Institute of Occupational Medicine (IOM) celebrates fifty years of endeavour to understand and prevent occupational and environmental ill health. In this book, the authors, all of whom have been intimately associated with the Institute, trace its history from foundation by the then National Coal Board in 1969, through achieving independence in 1990 to its present role as a unique, independent, self-funding occupational and environmental health charity. Over those fifty years there have been many achievements of international significance, and the authors describe these in individual chapters according to the different scientific specialties of the Institute's scientists. However, this should not obscure the overriding ethos of the Institute's research and consultative work, which is determinedly multidisciplinary and which is driven by a desire to prevent occupational and general environmental ill health. IOM has not been engaged in science simply to find and refine ever-more detailed answers to academic questions. Rather, its purpose has always been for its science to be applied to make a difference In both policy and practice.

The Institute's path has not always been smooth over the fifty years, and the story of the difficulties it has faced and overcome is told in the initial four chapters. This is a story of adaptation and imaginative evolution in face of changing times for research and services in occupational health. It tells of a change in emphasis from coal dust to nanoparticles, from predominantly preventive medical research to mainly provision of consultative, training and measurement services, from doing it all itself to international and national collaborations, and from a UK emphasis to an international presence, especially across Europe and in Singapore. Inevitably, difficulties lie ahead, but the desire to contribute to the wellbeing of society is and will remain the motivation of those who work in the Institute. Its reputation rests on its independence, the loyalty of its staff, the quality of its scientific output and of the services it provides, and the value of that output to those who seek its help or advice. These strengths we carry into our future to deliver our purpose.

Part 1

The History of IOM

1

Foundation and the Coal Board years: 1969 to 1990

Summary

The Institute of Occupational Medicine (IOM) was founded as a research charity in 1969 by the National Coal Board, primarily to complete its groundbreaking research on lung disease in coal workers. This was intended to advise on dust standards in coal mines that would significantly reduce risks to these workers, sitting alongside engineering and other measures being taken by the nationalised industry. But it had a wider remit related to ergonomic factors in mining and ultimately to helping reduce health and safety risks in industry generally. The Institute was led initially by the Coal Board's chief medical officer, Dr John Rogan, then by Dr David Muir until 1978. Dr Anthony Seaton then took over as Director, leading it towards independence in 1990.

The first twenty years of IOM, with considerable support from the European Communities, saw successful completion of the major objectives in lung disease, with quantification of the risks to miners of lung disease providing a scientific foundation for workplace standard-setting. The research led to an understanding that coal mining not only caused the specific disease known as coal workers' pneumoconiosis but also to an increased risk of chronic obstructive lung disease, a condition commonly caused by tobacco smoking. It put IOM at the forefront of international research into occupational lung disease. Over that period, also, important advances were made in the ergonomics of mining, especially in machine design and protection against the physical hazards of mining.

Alongside the coal research ran a stream of research into understanding how asbestos causes disease, which led to establishment of methods for predicting hazard from other, substitute fibrous materials. The final years of this period were marked by a steep decline in the UK coal industry and the closure of many mines, threatening the survival of IOM. This was countered by an expansion in the range of the research to many other industries and by a start to provision of scientific and training services. By the late 1980s, IOM scientists were publishing over fifty papers annually and the Institute was counted among the best known in its field worldwide. These measures, together with reduction in staff numbers and costs, as the Coal Board, now British Coal, and the asbestos industries approached their ends, allowed IOM to relaunch itself in 1990 as a self-funding, fully independent research charity.

Origins, and the Pneumoconiosis Field Research

Coal, exploited in Britain from Roman times, powered industry increasingly from the 16th century and was the fuel that drove the Industrial Revolution from the late 18th century. As with all disruptive technologies to follow, adverse effects were commented on, most notably the dangers to miners (who included women and small children until the mid-19th century) and the air pollution from small industrial concerns and domestic fires in cities.[1] Through the 19th and 20th centuries, the uses of coal increased, from making coke for the steel industry, feedstock for chemical and plastics industries, gas for lighting and domestic use, and providing the power for electricity production. With this, the burden on workers' health rose. The exploitation of women and children ceased after a groundbreaking Royal Commission of 1842, but the toll on miners continued at the hands of numerous mine owners. Largely unnoticed, in an era when tuberculosis was very common, was the fact that coal miners suffered particularly from lung disease, and medical opinion was divided on whether this was related to infection, often tuberculous, or rather was a consequence of dust exposure. However, in the 1920s x-ray machines became available to medicine and it became apparent that many miners were developing serious non-tuberculous lung disease, particularly in the South Wales coalfields. Research into these diseases started at Cardiff University and the United Kingdom's Medical Research Council (MRC) in the 1930s, and in 1945 the MRC set up its Pneumoconiosis Research Unit (PRU) in Penarth.

The work of the Cardiff researchers and the PRU led to definition of the different manifestations of the coal miners' disease, coal workers' pneumoconiosis (CWP),[2] appreciation of its extent in South Wales, and the realisation that it would be widespread through the UK coalfields. It was necessary for the coal industry to take active steps to prevent this disease, if only to reduce the burden on the State of paying the recently introduced compensation for disability. This proved a complex issue for an industry with, at that time,

Fig 1.1: British coal miner working on a coalface

hundreds of different employers. However, the election of the Labour Government under Clement Attlee in 1945 had led to nationalisation of the whole industry in 1946, the new National Coal Board (NCB) taking over 580 pits, fifty-five coke ovens, thirty smokeless fuel plants and over 800,000 workers [fig 1.1]. From this time, the responsibility for dealing with this problem, both in assessing its significance and extent and in preventing it, devolved to the NCB. It is noteworthy that this nationalisation preceded the National Health Service, and that the NCB instituted its own Medical and Radiological Service. Regular health surveys of all miners were commenced and, with advice from Professors Charles Fletcher and Archie Cochrane from the PRU, a research programme, the Pneumoconiosis Field Research (PFR), was started in 1953. The Chief Medical Officer of the NCB, an ex-army and MRC doctor, John Rogan, was its first Director [fig 1.2] and the programme was led by Dr JWJ Fay.[3] Based on the research findings of the PRU, its objectives were to find out:

Fig 1.2: Dr John Rogan, Chief Medical Officer of the National Coal Board and IOM's first Director 1969-72

- How much and what kinds of dust cause pneumoconiosis?
- What environmental conditions should be maintained if mineworkers are not to be disabled by the dust they breathe in the course of their work?

The researchers recruited some 50,000 coal miners from a representative twenty-five collieries across Britain, from Kent to Wales to Scotland, and started a programme of airborne coal dust measurement in all the pits. This was combined with five-yearly assessments of the miners by occupational and symptom questionnaires, lung function testing and chest radiography. The collieries were chosen to represent the range of mining and geological conditions in the country; thus started what was at the time the largest and most ambitious occupational epidemiological study ever carried out. This story is told in detail in chapter 5.

The foundation of IOM

The gathering of all these data on this large number of miners was difficult and ambitious enough; equally so, particularly in view of the computing facilities available in the 1960s, was the need to analyse them in such a way as to advise the industry on what dust standards were needed to prevent lung problems in the workforce. A dedicated team of researchers led by Fay was needed to oversee the quality of the data-gathering and to plan and carry out the analyses. To this end, as the third survey was underway, Rogan persuaded the NCB to found a separate institute in Edinburgh (the city in which he had obtained his medical degrees). The Institute of Occupational Medicine (IOM) was officially opened on 22 April 1969 by Lord Robens, chairman of the National Coal Board [fig 1.3]. It was located in purpose-built five-storey accommodation in central Edinburgh and was established as a research charity but with all staff employed by the NCB [fig 1.4]. The site was rented for a peppercorn annual sum from the University of Edinburgh. The independence of IOM was

Fig 1.3: The official opening of
IOM on 22 April 1969

guaranteed by its charitable status and its Management Board, of
which NCB senior management and Chief Medical Officer, the coal
trade unions and independent scientists were members. The original
scientist on the Board was Sir John Brotherston, Professor of Public
Health at Edinburgh University, later succeeded by Dr Una McLean,
Reader in Public Health, and then Sir Richard Doll, previously Regius
Professor of Medicine at Oxford and a world-leading epidemiologist.
IOM reported formally to the NCB Board and to a UK governmental
National Dust Prevention Committee which included senior members
of the regulatory department.

Fig 1.4: The original Institute building in Roxburgh Place, Edinburgh taken in 1977

The original senior staff

The NCB Chief Medical Officer, Rogan, was also the first Director of IOM until he retired in 1972. He was succeeded by Dr David Muir, who was a chest physician and physiologist and had been head of IOM's medical branch, responsible for the surveys [fig 1.5]. The other branches were environmental, statistics, pathology and ergonomics.

The original department heads were respectively Henry Walton OBE, Dr Michael Jacobsen, Dr John MG Davis and Tom Leamon. Walton was a distinguished physicist who had worked with JS Haldane, a pioneer of physiology [fig 1.6]. His studies for a PhD had been interrupted by war service, when he did fundamental research on respirators (gas masks) and aerosols. Out of this work had come the invention of the spinning disc method of producing experimental aerosols and the standard method for testing respirator efficiency, both of which are still in regular use in laboratories round the world. After the war he had joined the research laboratories of the National Coal Board and became Assistant Director responsible for the environmental research. He had worked on the basic mechanisms for measuring the critical fine (respirable) component of the dust generated in mines, and

Fig 1.5: Dr David Muir,
Director 1972-76

Fig 1.6: Henry Walton,
Head of Environmental Branch,
Interim Director 1976

with his colleague Bob Hamilton had built this into an instrument that would withstand the rigours of the mine environment, the MRE113a dust sampler (see chapter 6). This instrument is still used to control dust levels in mines and was the one to be used in the PFR, playing an essential role in making estimates of the dust exposures of the miners involved. He was also editor of a leading journal in his field, *Annals of Occupational Hygiene*.

Jacobsen was a mathematician and statistician, a pre-war refugee from Nazi Germany who after his first degree from London University had gained his PhD working on the PFR data [fig 1.7]. He was a cultured man with a very strong commitment to scientific rigour and to betterment of the conditions of the less fortunate. Davis was a pathologist who had been a research director in Cambridge and had acquired a reputation from his electron microscope work on the harmful effects of asbestos on the lungs [fig 1.8]. He was able to continue his research in IOM laboratories on the Bush estate south of Edinburgh where facilities for studies of dust inhalation were built by IOM's physics and technical staff. He was notable for his encouragement of his staff at all levels to further their careers by study and obtaining postgraduate qualification; he

Fig 1.7: Dr Michael Jacobsen, Head of Statistics Branch
(Taken at IOM's 40th Anniversary in 2009)

Fig 1.8: Dr John Davis, Head of Pathology Branch, with members of his staff

also had a strange obsession with building model aircraft. Leamon was an ergonomist interested in applying his discipline to the difficult working conditions in mines, his IOM laboratories being based in the NCB's Mining Research Establishment in Bretby, near Burton-on-Trent, Derbyshire. Each had a small team of scientists and technicians with secretarial support. Staff numbers rose from about fifty originally to approximately 180 as research income from European grants rose, including technicians employed on measurement of dust in the research collieries and a field team who carried out the medical surveys of the miners in a mobile laboratory [fig 1.9].

Fig 1.9: IOM Mobile epidemiology and x-ray laboratories (c.1980)

The watershed

A watershed moment occurred in the life of IOM in 1977 when Muir left to take an academic appointment in Canada, where he was able to initiate research on metal miners. Walton was appointed to the position of Director on an interim basis until a permanent replacement was found. Rogan's successor as NCB's, now British Coal's (BC), chief medical officer, Dr John McLintock, recruited Dr Anthony Seaton in January 1978 to take over as Director [fig 1.10].

Seaton was an experienced consultant chest physician in Cardiff with a doctorate in lung physiology who had worked at the University of West Virginia on coal miners' diseases. He had published a textbook on occupational lung diseases and was shortly to become editor of the medical journal, *Thorax*. But it was for the staff a worrying time, as the data from the PFR had been accumulated over 15 years and initial analyses had shown a relationship between dust exposure and risk of pneumoconiosis that had already been sufficient to guide British Coal in setting a dust standard. This work was the first key result from IOM's research and was published in the world's leading scientific journal, *Nature*.[4] It marked achievement of the original scientific and practical objectives, the *raison d'être* of IOM, and raised a question as to its future. But simultaneously it made the international reputation of IOM, since the data were used by the United States National Institute of Occupational Safety and Health to define a coal mine dust standard in that country and thus to guide other countries worldwide in monitoring preventive action.

The question confronting Seaton and the senior staff in 1978 was, where now? This was brought further into focus when, in 1979, Margaret Thatcher's Conservative Party won the general election on a policy that came to be characterised as neo-liberalism, with a pledge to reduce taxation and public spending. Clearly the nationalised mining industry, facing increasingly difficult mining conditions and competition from cheaper imported coal, was to be a target, and IOM was part of this.

Fig 1.10: Professor Anthony Seaton,
Director 1976-90

Management of IOM

The management structure of IOM at the time is relevant to how the difficulties were eventually overcome. The Director was responsible for both the research and the finance, and these were overseen by a monthly senior staff meeting, the detail of the finances being controlled by the Institute Secretary, Peter Osborne. He was a long-term NCB employee who had been a prisoner of war in Germany where he had been forced to work in coal mines; he was a talented artist who exhibited at the Scottish Royal Academy. Later his role was taken over by Dr Robert Bolton, a key member of the pathology branch who had to cease his laboratory work for medical reasons and took an MBA; he was to become responsible for the increasingly complex finances of IOM in the later 1980s. The overall control was by a Management Council as described above, chaired by a BC Board Member, to which Seaton reported annually. BC set an annual budget, and this and the work done within it were also reported formally to BC and its Chairman, Sir

Derek Ezra, each year. The original chair of the Council was Jimmy Cowan, Director of the BC Scottish Area, succeeded a few years later by Robert Dunn, BC Director of Mining.

It rapidly became obvious that the survival of IOM depended on keeping the goodwill of BC at a time when the industry was facing decimation or worse. This depended on reducing costs to BC and increasing the value of what was done for them. The strategy adopted towards the former was to increase work and thus funding from sources outwith the coal industry and gradually to lose staff, if possible by natural wastage. Increasing value came from emphasising the benefits of the ergonomic research in areas such as safety and design of equipment and machines, a major opportunity for winning European grants, as recounted in chapter 8. Research based on PFR results was difficult to justify to hard-pressed mining engineers in the then current climate, but it also provided a golden opportunity to obtain research funds from the European Communities' Coal and Steel research programmes and IOM was a major beneficiary of these, for both lung and ergonomic research.[5] Aside from this, the results of the PFR were responsible for the lowering of the coal mine dust standard and thus made a crucial contribution to reduction of pneumoconiosis among the miners. This and the publications flowing from it led to IOM being recognised as a world-leading centre for research into occupational dust diseases, attracting many overseas scientists to work and study in its Edinburgh laboratories. Several of these set up similar research programmes in their own countries, notably in the USA, Canada, Japan and Australia.

Evolution towards the modern IOM
Senior staff changes
IOM was very well equipped scientifically from its onset and further improvements were made with support from BC from the late 1970s. The medical branch was encouraged to look for research

that would enhance its national and international reputation in respiratory medicine, and Dr Colin Soutar, a chest physician trained in London but then working in Chicago, was recruited to head it. Later he was joined by a trainee, Dr Raymond Agius, a young chest physician; after qualifying also in occupational medicine and making a considerable contribution to the epidemiological research, he went as a senior lecturer to Edinburgh University, and later was appointed Professor of Occupational and Environmental Medicine at Manchester University. Henry Walton, after serving as Deputy Director, retired and his branch was divided into two: environmental and physics. Jim Dodgson, who had been Walton's deputy, took over the former. He had started his career as a school science teacher but had moved to the coal industry and had become a distinguished occupational hygienist. An academic physicist, Dr Jim Vincent, was recruited at Walton's suggestion from Strathclyde University to lead the latter. Vincent is also a talented pianist, both jazz and classical, frequently called on to perform professionally. BC was persuaded to purchase the spacious Forbes laboratory across the road from the head office to house the scientific equipment for these enlarged branches and to accommodate a large wind tunnel [fig 1.11]. Scanning and transmission electron microscopes were installed together with a wide range of chemical analytical equipment. Meanwhile Leamon moved to an academic post in the USA and was replaced as Head of Ergonomics by his deputy, Geoff Simpson.

Evolving research

Jacobsen's statistics branch, with two talented and able senior statisticians, Fintan Hurley and Dr Brian Miller, took the lead in further surveys and analyses of the PFR and other data, increasingly stimulated by medical questions from Soutar and Seaton. Major issues were the relationships between dust exposure and chronic obstructive lung disease (COPD, then referred to as chronic bronchitis and emphysema) and questions as to whether

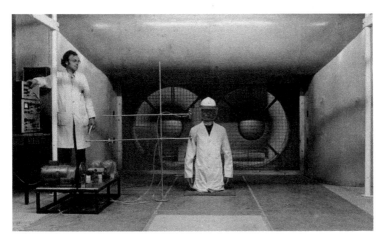

Fig 1.11: IOM large wind tunnel in the Forbes laboratory

pneumoconiosis progresses after dust exposure ceases and on the effects of quartz in coal dust. New studies were carried out in other industries, several of which informed government standard-setting, notably on the effects of inhalation of PVC for ICI, on the effects on the lungs of wool dust inhalation, and a programme of research on the health effects of the by then extinct Scottish shale oil industry for the USA Department of Energy (see chapter 5).

The performance on time and budget of these important studies benefited from Seaton's decision in the early 1980s to formalise multidisciplinary work on almost all projects, something that was probably unique in academic research in the UK at the time. IOM was able to call on medical, statistical, pathological, physical, chemical and environmental expertise for its projects, all of which were obliged to have a named leader from any level in the hierarchy and to involve scientists and technicians from other relevant branches from the planning stage. Leaders were required to report progress regularly to the senior staff meeting. Staff at all levels (including technical) were encouraged to formulate projects, aiming to increase opportunities and release talent among younger staff.

In academic terms, the pathology branch under Davis made an enormous contribution to the international and national reputation of IOM (see chapter 7). Their inhalational and cellular research laboratories were enabled to move to two redundant cottages at the City Hospital in Edinburgh for no rent, in return for consultant physician services provided by Seaton and Soutar. The coal research was led by Dr Anne Ruckley and ultimately solved the riddle of coal and emphysema: the more coal dust a miner inhales, the greater the likelihood he will have significant emphysema. [fig 1.12] [6] This, with the epidemiology from the PFR, proved a key factor in later persuading the Industrial Injuries Advisory Council that miners with sufficient dust exposure should receive compensation for chronic obstructive lung disease (see chapter 5). The asbestos research, funded by the Asbestosis Research Council (with appropriate guarantees of freedom to publish), and with a major contribution from Bolton, produced many papers, most notably on the characteristics of fibres that produce the diseases asbestosis and mesothelioma.[7] From this came a remarkable succession of PhDs for young researchers, including six who had originally started as technicians. One of these, Ken Donaldson, later became a world authority on fibre toxicology and Professor of Respiratory Toxicology at Edinburgh University. The asbestos research led to contracts to study other fibres being produced as substitutes, information invaluable in preventing replication in industry of the well-known hazards of asbestos itself (see chapter 6).

Fig 1.12: Post-mortem section of coal miner's lung showing white areas of emphysema as well as black coal deposits

An early problem for the research was access to computing. Initially IOM had a landline telephone link to the NCB's computer, in the English Midlands, and employed a team of programmers in Edinburgh. In the early 1980s, at the instigation of Bob Steele, Head of Programming, BC was persuaded to purchase a mainframe computer for the headquarters building in Edinburgh, which greatly facilitated the work. At the same time, it became apparent that it would be necessary to set up a commercial arm, principally to sell services on occupational hygiene and chemical analyses to industry; Dodgson's deputies, Alan Bradley and Dr Alastair Robertson, took on this role (see chapter 3). From the start, IOM also had staff concerned mainly with dust exposure measurement in four outstations in England and Wales. As the work on the PFR declined they either retired or turned their attention to looking for other environmental measurement work in their areas (see chapter 3). Increasingly this related to asbestos, and the Edinburgh laboratories developed a major expertise and international role in this area.[8]

Walton and his younger physicist colleague, Dr Steve Beckett, had earlier patented a microscope eyepiece with an etched graticule that enabled accurate sizing of fibres and, under the leadership of physicist Dr Nigel Crawford in the environmental branch, both national and international schemes for standardising asbestos/fibre counting were set up, putting IOM at the centre of this worldwide (see chapter 3). The physics branch under Vincent made major advances in measurement of dust of different sizes and shapes in aerosols and patented several instruments; one of these, the IOM personal inhalable dust sampler, became a standard piece of equipment. Vincent and his physicist colleagues also worked closely with the pathology branch to understand the properties of fibrous aerosols and investigate them experimentally (see chapters 6 and 7).

The ergonomists in their Bretby laboratories were more closely associated with the day-to-day work of mining (see chapter 8). They embraced several scientific disciplines including engineering, noise, vibration and temperature, and developed a wide range of projects directed at safer and more efficient operation in the difficult conditions of British coal mines. They made important contributions to improving the design of mining machinery at a time when Scotland was a major exporter of such specialised machines, for which IOM won national awards, also described in chapter 8.

By the end of the 1980s IOM was thriving, its reputation high in the worlds of occupational medicine, occupational hygiene, particle toxicology, epidemiology and ergonomics. Its staff had been reduced to about 120 and it was publishing over fifty scientific papers and many technical documents each year, contributing to occupational health preventive standards across industry in the UK. The value of this to regulators and to public health was widely recognised and advice on preventing dust diseases was given by members of staff round the world, notably in India and China. IOM had progressively reduced its dependence on BC for funding from about 75% to about 30%. But the coal industry had suffered a disastrous strike and the National Union of Mineworkers had been defeated; the end of nationalisation was in sight and with it the viability of IOM and its core funding.

A start to scientific services and teaching

Despite the success of the research programme, the pressures on the coal industry meant that the money available from BC to support the research was reduced significantly year-on-year. Research grants did not generally provide for overhead expenses at the time, so IOM started in the mid-1980s to sell expertise and measurement services to industry and government bodies wherever possible (see chapter 3). Seaton also started to provide expert independent evidence for lawyers in relation to industrial diseases other than those thought to be related to coal. In addition, IOM started teaching undergraduate medical students and postgraduate doctors, first contributing to an established course at Dundee University. Later, this became a joint Aberdeen University/ IOM diploma and MSc course. From the late 1980s, training and

MSc courses for occupational hygienists were started, again jointly with Aberdeen. The medical teaching, though not very profitable, did have the advantage of spreading knowledge of IOM among a potentially influential group of occupational physicians. The selling of scientific expertise, however, became an increasingly important part of IOM's future and ultimately key to its survival.

Separation from British Coal

By 1987 it had become apparent that IOM's future with BC was likely to be limited, as mines were closing across Britain and its role in investigating pneumoconiosis was of little further benefit to the UK industry, the pneumoconiosis problem being largely under control in this country. Moreover, the research results had by then clearly indicated that coal dust exposure also contributed to the risk of chronic obstructive lung disease, indicating that further reduction of the dust standard in mines would be necessary. The relatively sympathetic chairmen of the Management Council, mining engineer Robert Dunn and his successor, retired civil servant Sir Kenneth Couzens, had retired and been replaced by a much less sympathetic BC Board Member, mining engineer Dr Ken Moses. Seaton, in order to build an academic link, had obtained a half-time post as Professor of Environmental and Occupational Medicine at Aberdeen University, and joint postgraduate teaching programmes with that university had been set up. However, in 1988 Moses visited IOM with the intention of closing it and making all the staff redundant. This was a shock to the staff and was resisted by Seaton who was summarily suspended after one of the affected staff members, unknown to him, attracted headlines in the local Edinburgh press about the threatened closure. Supported by Sir Richard Doll FRS (who was then the academic member of the Management Council), Seaton appealed to the then Chairman of BC, Sir Ian McGregor, and was given the opportunity of doing a deal with Moses. Various options had already been explored, including being taken over by Edinburgh or Aberdeen universities or by a commercial concern related to occupational health, but none had proved viable; independence as a research charity with a commercial arm seemed the only remaining option, and this is what Seaton presented to Moses.

Agreement was reached that BC would make an initial grant to IOM of the sum it would otherwise have spent over three years, roughly £3 million, in order to complete the current BC and EC research contracts. Seaton negotiated a very generous grant from a charity, the Colt Foundation, of £0.5 million, and with Davis visited the major manufacturers of non-asbestos fibres to raise a further £0.5 million, these grants allowing the formation of a Colt Fibre Research Programme to investigate possible toxicity of new fibres. The senior staff agreed that it would also be necessary to reduce staff costs and that Soutar would take over the role of Director, all the others agreeing to take redundancy and nominate their successors. Jacobsen obtained academic posts in Germany and the USA. Vincent obtained a university chair in the USA and Davis and Dodgson retired. Most of the ergonomists transferred to work for British Coal at Bretby but some key personnel transferred to Edinburgh. Seaton continued at Aberdeen University but with the help of Bolton set up a fund-raising trust for IOM which in due course purchased the land on which the IOM building stood from Edinburgh University. In April 1990 the new IOM was launched as an independent self-funding charity.

Chapter 1: References and Notes

1. The story of coal exploitation and the harmful consequences is told in Seaton A. (2018). *Farewell King Coal; from industrial triumph to climatic disaster*. Edinburgh, Dunedin Academic.
2. Pneumoconiosis is a term for lung disease caused usually by inhalation of mineral dust such as coal, asbestos or quartz. Exposure to coal and quartz causes first nodular (snow storm-

like) appearances on the chest radiograph. With increasing exposure these become more profuse and aggregate together to form large masses destructive of lung tissue called progressive massive fibrosis.

3. Fay JWJ. (1957). The National Coal Board's pneumoconiosis field research. *Nature*; 180: 309-310.

4. Jacobsen M, Rae S, Walton WH, Rogan J. (1970). New dust standards for British coal mines. *Nature*; 227: 445-447.

5. The Coal and Steel Community was one of the original Communities that led to the formation of the European Union. It recognised the importance at the time of these two industries to the European economy, and each member country paid a levy from its coal and steel companies to develop the industry across the countries. Thus, the IOM was in the position of having to make research bids to Europe in order to recoup this money, especially in lung disease and ergonomic research. Having nationalised industries and a dedicated research institute was very much to the UK's advantage, allowing IOM to become a European leader.

6. Emphysema is a disease of the lungs in which the walls of the smallest air compartments break down, reducing the area available for gas exchange and reducing the natural elasticity of the lungs. It is a key component of the disease known as chronic obstructive pulmonary disease (COPD). See chapter 6.

7. Asbestos-caused diseases became a major health issue from the 1960s when the mineral was shown to cause an invariably fatal cancer of the lung lining or pleura called mesothelioma. A chronic fibrosis of the lungs themselves, asbestosis, had been known among asbestos workers from the 1900s but mesothelioma seemed to occur after much lower dust exposures, sometimes in people who were only incidentally exposed.

8. While coal dust can be caught on a filter and be weighed, the harmfulness of asbestos seemed to depend on the number of fibres of a particular size that are inhaled and

retained in the lung. This means that they must be counted under a microscope. Research on this at IOM is described in subsequent chapters. As the use of asbestos was being prohibited in the UK, other substitute fibres were being introduced and IOM research increasingly considered the possible toxicity of such substitutes.

2

The independent Institute: 1990 to 2005

Summary

The new Institute of Occupational Medicine, now fully independent and self-funding, was presented with three major challenges: financial, the need for continuity after the end of current limited-term research contracts, and maintenance of quality in the context of financial pressure. To overcome these challenges required administrative change and tight financial management but also the need rapidly to develop income sources other than existing grants while maintaining an international research profile. The public service ethos of the old IOM was maintained, and the original research leaders were succeeded by able up-coming scientists under the leadership of Dr Colin Soutar; a wider profile of research into occupational and environmental health was developed to replace the traditional coal and asbestos studies. At the same time the services and consultancies were expanded considerably. In 2003 the old IOM headquarters building was sold, and the staff and laboratories moved to a newly constructed building in the Heriot Watt University Research Park.

Becoming independent

On 1 April 1990 IOM finally emerged as a fully independent, self-funding research charity under Scots Law, a Company Limited by Guarantee. This transformation from ownership by a public body, British Coal, was a unique and certainly risky venture in the world of scientific research. The obstacles to success were considerable, not least the loss of most of the senior staff, all of whom had international reputations in their fields. The loss of guaranteed core funding was partly offset by the grant agreed by British Coal to enable completion of the European-supported coal-related and ergonomic research and by the grants obtained by Professor Anthony Seaton and Dr John Davis towards transfer of the asbestos research to the investigation of other fibrous materials of value to industry. But this was far from sufficient to ensure an easy translation to independence.

A new Board of Management was established under the leadership of Dr Colin Soutar, who had previously been head of Medical Branch, as Chief Executive [fig 2.1]. The Board comprised

Fig 2.1: Colin Soutar, Chief Executive 1990-2005

the heads of departments: Dr Rob Bolton, now Marketing Director; Alan Bradley, Director of Occupational Hygiene; Dr Nigel Crawford, Director of Quality Assurance and Physics, Fintan Hurley, Director of Risk Sciences; Dr Raymond Agius, Director of Medical Services; Dr Alastair Robertson, Director of Laboratory Services; and Alex Traynor, Commercial Director, who had transferred from British Coal. The Board invited Russell Griggs from Scottish Enterprise, who had played a critical role in establishing the new company, to chair the Board meetings and to be the first legal Director (Governor). In early years Griggs was instrumental in fostering a more commercial attitude amongst the other members of the Board. Griggs, Sir William Simpson, retired Chairman of the Health and Safety Commission, and Professor Philip Love, then of Aberdeen University and later to be Vice Chancellor of Liverpool University, generously agreed to be Governors (unpaid Directors). Some years later, as Sir William Simpson retired, Sir Frank Davies, a more recent Chairman of the Health and Safety Commission, joined the Governors. Informally it was agreed that the management and direction of IOM would be the responsibility of the Board of Management. As well as Traynor, Derek Walker, Financial Controller, and Maureen Quinn, Personnel Officer, also joined IOM from British Coal. Altogether, the staff of the new IOM was over one hundred.

All previous employees had been made redundant by British Coal in case the new IOM were to fail. The loss of the senior staff reduced the salary costs somewhat, and the pay and conditions of remaining staff were renegotiated, leading to small percentage reductions in salary uniformly across the board. This acceptance by almost all the staff exemplified their loyalty and dedication to the ideals of IOM (an earlier, possibly apocryphal, story was that careers advice by an external body was "don't apply there, nobody ever leaves").

Ongoing research and service contracts were transferred from the old IOM, including the Colt and mineral fibre grants to develop a programme of research into substitutes for asbestos. Working capital was provided by a loan from the Bank of Scotland. Previously only direct costs had been charged to clients but now realistic overhead charges of 160% of staff costs had to be added to prices. For ongoing contracts, British Coal, the Health and Safety Executive (HSE), the Colt Foundation and the industry sponsors of the Colt Fibre Research Programme, the National Federation of Heavy Clay Industries, among others, understandingly accepted this increase.

The Board reaffirmed the policy of independence, impartiality, integrity and freedom to publish research, more formally "For the benefit of those at work and in the community, the purpose being to provide quality research, consultancy and teaching services in health, hygiene and safety, and to maintain an independent position as an international centre of scientific excellence". A culture of delegation and promotion of enterprise and initiative at all levels was encouraged, to assist commitment and bring as many minds as possible to addressing the challenges ahead.

Managing the new IOM

At the time of independence, IOM faced three related threats: financial, reputational and the need to replace time-limited projects. As a charity it did not have shareholders but clearly had to survive financially while maintaining a quality of work that would enable it to continue to attract grants and sell services. This depended on keeping high-quality scientists and equipping them appropriately. Funding from the coal industry and from associated European grants was time-limited, and the UK base of heavy industry, which had looked to IOM for health-related research, was being eroded through the 1990s. Early idealistic discussions on the appropriate balance between research and services were overtaken by recognition of the hard reality, that the balance would be determined by what work could be won in open competition and that the aim should be for both activities to thrive. To protect the charitable status of IOM, a subsidiary company, IOM Consulting, was formed to conduct the services and consultancies, any profits from it to be donated to the parent charitable company.

A time-based project management system was inherited from the original IOM. A financial system was established, and personnel policies designed. Unions were not recognised for the purposes of collective bargaining. Instead two committees were set up that included elected staff members: a Joint Review Council that discussed terms, conditions and salaries, and a Consultative Committee that considered all other IOM matters. The existing matrix management system was retained, meaning that specialist staff from any department could easily be brought in as required to multidisciplinary research projects. However, it later became apparent that the services and consultancy work was usually single discipline.

Bolton, an outstanding scientist whose Edinburgh PhD was one of the first to have been gained at IOM, had acquired a part-time MBA and been moved to the post of IOM Secretary prior to independence. He had produced a business plan for the new IOM, and now met and visited many organisations promoting IOM's independence, quality and skills in occupational epidemiology and exposure assessment.

In its first year of independence IOM made a profit, but a loss in the second year led to the need for six redundancies. Additional procedures for project supervision by senior staff were introduced to assist quality and cost control, and more frequent one-to-one meetings between the Chief Executive and department heads were established. Subsequently break-even or small annual profits were made.

The development of the research is described briefly here but mainly in chapters 5-9. The successful development of the services and consultancies of IOM under the direction of Alastair

Robertson is described in chapter 3. Crawford developed and maintained contracts with the Health and Safety Executive (HSE) for national and international schemes for quality assurance in fibre measurement (the RICE project – see chapter 3). Dr Richard Love, a physiologist who had succeeded Agius in running the Medical Services, managed occupational epidemiology studies initially (before retiring to become a well-known figure in the world of dry-stane dyking) and Bradley, who had become an expert in asbestos hazards, took over the Occupational Hygiene Services. In later years the structure and main team was simplified to Research led by Hurley, Services and Consultancies led by Robertson, and Commercial led by Traynor, Soutar remaining Chief Executive. When Traynor left he was replaced by John Allan, previously from Scottish and Newcastle, as Commercial Director.

IOM's research ethos

Importantly, there had been from the foundation of IOM a commitment to investigate with an open mind and report openly what was found, as formulated originally by Dr Michael Jacobsen. Funding for research was accepted only on the understanding that results, and IOM's interpretation of them, would be reported publicly. Investigating 'with an open mind' does not mean hypothesis-free investigation (applied research does not happen in a vacuum, but in a context of suggestive results indicating potential relationships); rather, it means being open-minded about what the new work may suggest, not leaning towards one conclusion or another because of source of funding, or external pressure, or previous commitment to a particular theory or viewpoint. This was formalised in the later years of IOM as a commitment to the values of *independence, impartiality and integrity*, but this formulation was making explicit long-standing values of IOM's research. These also became values of its services and consulting work, as these were developed over time.

The research from IOM's earliest years had been inter-disciplinary, not just multidisciplinary, and included the important principle it be relevant to development of policy. While in fact fundamental scientific advances were made at IOM, for example in measurement techniques and in understanding mechanisms of disease (especially related to inhaled particles), IOM was not designed for nor in general funded for 'blue-skies' curiosity-driven research. The point was to do what it took to answer the question well, and in a timescale that supported the development of policy, either governmental or industrial. A focus on the team rather than on the individual researcher (regardless of high international reputation) created a context where different disciplines were not just represented, but scientists collaborated in understanding from different viewpoints what was going on, how to investigate it, and how to interpret the findings. Nor was the focus on a research team to the detriment of individual careers. The development of individuals' scientific reputations was encouraged, but within the context of the effectiveness and good reputation of the whole IOM. Understanding of the benefits of the research to society at large also meant that many researchers stayed long-term, despite opportunities elsewhere. Others who moved on often maintained collaborative links with IOM.

The changing research profile

Applied contract research responds to practical needs for information as perceived by potential funding bodies. Such bodies include government departments, European research programmes, industry associations and large companies. If the research achieves its aims, the need is satisfied, and the funding moves on to new, sometimes consequential, requirements; or it ceases. Research contractors need to be agile and flexible to maintain continuity of work. A detailed description of the progress of the research over fifty years is given in Part 2. A brief overview of the period 1990-2005 is given below.

Research development

Despite the pressures, IOM scientists continued to publish research results in reports, peer review journals and conference proceedings. Published IOM final research reports and reports by other bodies of IOM work are a guide to the preceding funded research contracts.[1] Inspection over the period 1990-2004 reveals striking changes, but also some continuity. With the decline and privatisation of the coal industry, research into dust control methods and scale modelling of the behaviour of dusts and gases in mines declined and ceased. The work on development of air samplers diminished.[2] The Fibre Research Programme supported by the Colt Foundation, the European Insulation Manufacturers Association and the European Ceramic Fibre Industry Association was successfully completed, describing the fibre dimensions and their ability to withstand dissolution in lungs that determine toxicity.[3-5] Toxicological and rodent biopersistence[6] studies then ceased, and the HSE-supported method development in measuring minerals was also completed.

Occupational epidemiological and exposure-response studies,[7] though diminished, held up well, though the decision of the Health and Safety Executive (HSE) to take these in-house during the period removed a major source of funding for this kind of work. HSE did continue to support studies of exposures and related methods, as well as some epidemiological studies based on data held by IOM.

A growth area led by Dr Lang Tran, a mathematician recruited to work with the toxicologists, was mathematical modelling of the physiological and pathological responses to a range of dust types: inert dusts, fibres, coal dusts and silica,[8-11] as recorded in chapter 7. Studies of occupational exposures and methods of assessment continued to flourish under the leadership of Drs John Cherrie and Rob Aitken, two young physicists whose contributions would be central to the future development of IOM (see chapters 6 and 9). These were funded by HSE and some metal industry associations, the focus moving from airborne to dermal exposures.[12,13] Later in the period, studies of environmental exposure to pollutants started to grow, including traffic-generated pollutants, environmental asbestos risks around certain factories, and participation in review of government policy. Studies of human factors and heat stress at work increased under Dr Richard Graveling, notably in firefighters,[14,15] work funded by the UK Government Home Office (chapter 8).

Epidemiological studies

Occupational epidemiology led by Hurley and Soutar, historically the major component of IOM research, though reduced, continued at a substantial level, described in detail in chapter 5. The records of the Pneumoconiosis Field Research proved a valuable resource for investigating on behalf of HSE the quantitative relationship between mineral dust exposure and lung functional deficits, work that was later extended to consider the applicability of these risk estimates to chemically inert insoluble dusts in general.[16] The National Federation of Clay Industries supported an exposure-response study of lung radiological changes and exposure to quartz in brick manufacturing.[17,18]

Not uncommonly, industrial activities give rise to health concerns among local communities from exposure to pollution, and such concerns can be addressed by specific epidemiological studies, for which IOM was and is well qualified and its independence respected. For example, an opencast coal mine was subject to complaints of asthma in the adjacent community, and the industry body, Opencast, commissioned an epidemiological study of workers within several opencast sites.[19] HSE commissioned exposure-response studies of the relation between dusts containing quartz and risks of respiratory symptoms and evidence of silicosis[20] in hard rock quarry workers, and the risks of respiratory symptoms, lung function and lung radiological changes in relation to exposure to wool dust in workers

Fig 2.2: Operative in the wool spinning industry (c.1980)

in the wool textile industry [fig 2.2].[21] British Steel, responding to concerns about respiratory ill health in its workers in steel mills, commissioned a study in current workers of respiratory symptoms and cardiac risk factors in relation to occupations graded by dust exposure.[22] The European Ceramic Fibre Industries Association commissioned a study of workers in European fibre manufacturing factories conducted jointly with INSERM, the French National Research Institute.[23]

In the late 1980s, concern was expressed in the media and among agricultural workers about farmers suffering acute symptoms and long-term neurological illness after dipping sheep with organophosphorus pesticides (to prevent infestations). The Ministry of Agriculture, Farming and Fisheries commissioned a study[24] to investigate this, described in chapter 5 [fig 2.3]. The results led to official guidance on safe practice. Responding also to concerns that exposure of soldiers to aerosols of depleted uranium from missiles during the Iraq War had led to chronic uranium poisoning, the Ministry of Defence commissioned a study of uranium levels in the urine of returning soldiers, in collaboration

Fig 2.3: Chucker manoeuvring sheep into the dipping bath (1999)

with the Institute of Naval Medicine.[25] Other industries and workers investigated over this period included agriculture, semiconductor manufacturing, polyvinylchloride manufacturing and, for possible exposure to benzene, the petroleum industry.

Later, in the 1990s, environmental epidemiological studies grew. Between 1995 and 2000, the Soufrière Hills volcano on the island of Montserrat erupted, forcing evacuation of the capital city, Plymouth, which was buried by hot dust. The UK Department of Health, which was responsible for public health in the colony, commissioned studies led by Dr Alison Searl, a geology PhD who had joined IOM in 1995 as Head of Laboratory Services, of the airborne dust and its composition and toxicity, and of the exposed population [fig 2.4].[26,27] Finally, increasing public and media concern about air pollution was a characteristic of the early 2000s, and Hurley and Miller at IOM became active in advising UK Government committees on the harmful effects on health. IOM was increasingly involved in collaborative European projects assessing the health impacts of the fuel cycles. More locally, IOM was commissioned by the Scottish Office to investigate the likely impact of air pollution on mortality in Central Scotland.[28]

Fig 2.4: Dust cloud from the eruption of the Soufrière Hills
volcano in Montserrat (1997)

Expansion of the services and consultancies

A key development in this period was the development of commercial services and consultancies. The benefits to both research and consultancies were overall maintenance of the flow of work even though this might fluctuate in some areas; the ability to keep highly skilled personnel who could sometimes be deployed on either research or consultancy; and the sharing of fixed overhead costs. Under Robertson's direction, this aspect of IOM's activities expanded substantially, in Scotland and in outstations in England. Chapter 3 describes the progress of thriving activities including occupational hygiene, occupational health, asbestos, mineral and chemical analysis, ergonomics, safety, environmental impact assessments, provision of expert witness evidence, environmental monitoring, teaching and training, respirator and protective clothing testing, chemical health risk assessments and the asbestos fibre counting proficiency scheme.

Looking back

The period 1990 to 2005 had been particularly challenging for research with loss of funding from traditional industries after independence. Nevertheless, IOM adapted its research profile and was successful in broadening the range of those who sponsored the research while narrowing the previously broad scientific scope to areas of specific strength.

Great credit is due for this achievement in maintaining its research profile to those scientists[29], many younger, who won grants and led research, while building national and international reputations over this period. It is important also to recognise the vital contribution of those staff[30] who worked on services and consultancies under Robertson. All this work, research and services, depended on teams which included many other talented and dedicated members of staff, too numerous to mention but upon whose dedication and hard work the success of the new IOM was founded.

Moving to the new headquarters

A temporary IOM Trust had been set up in 1990 to raise charitable funds, led by Seaton and Bolton. This realised only small amounts of money, but enough for purchase from Edinburgh University of the freehold of the land on which the original building stood. The building itself, in Roxburgh Place in central Edinburgh, was originally the property of British Coal and had been donated with all the contents, including scientific equipment, to the new IOM at the time of transfer. It became apparent that this ageing and compartmentalised five-storey office building needed replacement or refurbishment. Led by Soutar and Allan, the old building was sold and a new internally networked open-plan building was constructed in the Research Park at Heriot Watt University in western Edinburgh. Scottish Enterprise gave helpful advice and a project management company was engaged. Design was modern and in a pleasant semi-rural setting. It was completed on time and budget, costing £3 million. IOM transferred in November 2003 [fig 2.5].

Fig 2.5: IOM HQ building at Riccarton

Influencing health and safety

From the beginning, IOM current and former staff had played a wider role in the world of occupational and environmental health. In the 1980s both Seaton and Walton edited international journals, *Thorax* and *Annals of Occupational Hygiene*; a former member of staff, Dr Trevor Ogden, took over the latter journal. Many served on UK and EU committees: Expert Panel on Air Quality Standards, Committee on the Medical Effects of Air Pollutants, Advisory Committee on Toxic Substances of the HSE, the Advisory Committee on Pesticides, Health and Safety Committees of Billiton and BHP Billiton. Occasional work overseas included consultancies for the International Labour Organization and UK Department for International Development.

An important development in the early 1990s was the recognition by the World Health Organization (WHO) of the work on international standardisation of asbestos fibre counting, leading to IOM becoming a WHO Collaborating Centre in Occupational Health. Over the subsequent years IOM's role as a WHO Collaborating Centre broadened into many wider linkages between IOM's expertise in occupational health and the WHO programme for occupational health worldwide, in exposure assessment, nanomaterials and human factors, while in parallel multiple connections were developed also on issues of environment and health.

A new Chief Executive

In 2005, after leading IOM through fifteen transformative years, Soutar retired to add a mathematics degree to his medical qualifications, and to scull and coach at a local rowing club. He was succeeded by two people: Dr Phil Woodhead as Chief Executive and Hurley as Scientific Director.

Chapter 2: References and Notes

1. Institute of Occupational Medicine. Staff publications list. Unpublished. Enquiries about IOM publications should be made to publications@iom-world.org.
2. An air sampler is a device that measures the average concentration in air of a pollutant over a defined period. Measurement over a full shift often gives lower average values than measurement over a short period timed to coincide with a task associated with high release of pollutant.
3. Biopersistence refers to the rate of dissolution of a particle in the lung milieu.
4. Searl A, Buchanan D, Cullen RT, Jones AD, Miller BG, Soutar CA. (1999). Biopersistence and durability of nine mineral fibre types in rat lungs over 12 months. *Annals of Occupational Hygiene*; 43: 143-153.
5. Miller BG, Jones AD, Searl A, Buchanan D, Cullen RT, Soutar CA, Davis JMG, Donaldson K. (1999). Influence of characteristics of inhaled fibres on development of tumours in the rat lung. *Annals of Occupational Hygiene*; 43: 167-179.
6. Miller BG, Searl A, Davis JMG, Donaldson K, Cullen RT, Bolton RE, Buchanan D, Soutar CA. (1999). Influence of fibre

length, dissolution and biopersistance on the production of mesothelioma in the rat peritoneal cavity. *Annals of Occupational Hygiene*; 43: 155-166.

7. Exposure is the product of the average concentration experienced by a worker and the duration of contact, often measured over a shift.

8. Mathematical modelling in this context describes quantitatively the behaviour of the inhalation of particles related to their physical properties, their dissolution if this occurs, and the responses of defensive cells in the lung leading to tissue damage.

9. Tran CL, Jones AD, Cullen RT, Donaldson K. (1999). Mathematical modelling of the retention and clearance of low-toxicity particles in the lung. *Inhalation Toxicology*; 11: 1059-1076.

10. Tran CL, Buchanan D, Cullen RT, Searl A, Jones AD, Donaldson K. (2000). Inhalation of poorly soluble particles. Influence of particle surface area on inflammation and clearance. *Inhalation Toxicology*; 12: 1113-1126.

11. Tran CL, Jones AD. (2003). Modelling the retention and clearance of man-made vitreous fibres in the rat lung. Inhalation Toxicology; 15: 553-587.

12. Cherrie JW, Robertson A. (1995) Biologically relevant assessment of dermal exposure. *Annals of Occupational Hygiene*; 39: 387-392.

13. Creely KS, Tickner J, Soutar AJ, Hughson GW, Pryde DE, Warren ND, Rae R, Money C, Phillips A, Cherrie JW. (2004). Evaluation and further development of EASE model 2.0. *Annals of Occupational Hygiene*; 49: 135-145.

14. Graveling RA, Johnstone JBG, Butler DM, Crawford J, Love RG, Maclaren WM, Ritchie P. (1999). Study of the degree of protection afforded by firefighters' clothing. London: Home Office Fire Research and Development Group. (Research Report Number 1/99).

15. Graveling RA, Stewart A, Cowie HA, Tesh KM, George JPK. (2001). Physiological and environmental aspects of firefighter training. London: Office of the Deputy Prime Minister. Fire Research Division. (Research Report Number 1/2001).

16. Cowie HA, Miller BG, Rawbone RG, Soutar CA. (2006). Dust related risks of clinically relevant lung functional deficits. *Occupational and Environmental Medicine*; 63: 320-325.

17. Love RG, Waclawski ER, Maclaren WM, Wetherill GZ, Groat SK, Porteous RH, Soutar CA. (1999). Risks of respiratory disease in the heavy clay industry. *Occupational and Environmental Medicine*; 57: 569-574.

18. Miller BG, Soutar CA. (2007). Observed and predicted silicosis risks in heavy clay workers. *Occupational Medicine*; 57: 569-574.

19. Love RG, Miller BG, Groat SK, Hagen S, Cowie HA, Johnston PP, Hutchison PA, Soutar CA. (1997). Respiratory health effects of opencast coalmining: a cross sectional study of current workers. *Occupational and Environmental Medicine*; 54: 416-423.

20. Silicosis is a progressive scarring of the lungs due to inhalation of dusts containing crystalline quartz (silica). It may lead to disability, even death.

21. Love RG, Muirhead M, Collins HPR, Soutar CA. (1991). The characteristics of respiratory ill health of wool textile workers. *British Journal of Industrial Medicine*; 48: 221-228.

22. Miller BG, Donnan PT, Sinclair A, Edwards JC, Soutar CA, Hurley JF. (1996). The respiratory and cardiovascular health of iron and steel process workers. Part II: results of the field studies and of the analyses of the data. Edinburgh: Institute of Occupational Medicine. (IOM Report TM/96/05).

23. Cowie HA, Wild P, Beck J, Auburtin G, Piekarski C, Massin N, Cherrie JW, Hurley JF, Miller BG, Groat S, Soutar CA. (2001). An epidemiological study of the respiratory health of workers in the European refractory ceramic fibre industry. *Occupational and Environmental Medicine*; 58: 800-810.

24. Pilkington A, Buchanan D, Jamal GA, Gillham R, Hansen S, Kidd M, Hurley JF, Soutar CA. (2001). An epidemiological study of the relations between exposure to organophosphate pesticides and indices of chronic peripheral neuropathy and neuropsychological abnormalities in sheep farmers and dippers. *Occupational and Environmental Medicine*; 58: 702-710.

25. Miller BG, Colvin AP, Hutchison PA, Tait H, Dempsey S, Lewis D, Soutar CA. (2007). A normative study of levels of uranium in the urine of British Forces personnel. *Occupational and Environmental Medicine*; 65: 398-403.

26. Searl A, Nicholl A, Baxter PJ. (2002). Assessment of the exposure of islanders to ash from the Soufrière Hills volcano, Montserrat, British West Indies. *Occupational and Environmental Medicine*; 59: 523-531.

27. Cowie HA, Graham MK, Searl A, Miller BG, Hutchison PA, Swales C, Dempsey S, Russell M. (2002). A health survey of workers on the island of Montserrat. Edinburgh: Institute of Occupational Medicine. (IOM Report TM/02/02).

28. Searl A, Hurley F, Holland M, King K, Stedman J, Vincent K. (2003). Quantifying the health impacts of pollutants emitted in Central Scotland. Web published: Scottish Executive. https://www.webarchive.org.uk/wayback/archive/20141202020205/http://www.scotland.gov.uk/Publications/2004/07/19640/40214

29. Notably Aitken, Cherry, Hilary Cowie, Graveling, Hurley, Alan Jones, Love, Miller, Adele Pilkington, Peter Ritchie, Searl, Soutar and Tran.

30. Notably Gilbert Armstrong, Bolton, Bradley, Crawford, Stuart Goddard, Graveling, Sheila Groat, Steve Janssen, Arthur Johnston, Alan Jones, Searl, Adele Pilkington, Jerry Slann, Geoff Smith, Jane Tierney and many others. Note that several individuals were active in both research and consultancies.

3

Commercial development: 1970 to 2005

Summary

The Institute of Occupational Medicine started undertaking consultancy and service work in the early 1970s. This work has grown hugely and has comprised more than two thirds of IOM's business since the late 1990s, rising to three quarters by 2005. It has covered most areas of IOM's scientific expertise, including occupational hygiene, occupational health, asbestos, mineral and chemical analysis, ergonomics, safety, environmental impact assessments, provision of expert witness evidence, environmental monitoring, teaching and training, respirator and protective clothing testing, chemical health risk assessments and the RICE asbestos fibre counting proficiency scheme. IOM consultancies have been delivered in the UK, Ireland and across the world, into Asia, North and South America, Africa and continental Europe.

Services and consultancies in the 1970s

The start was modest. The skills developed in research activities were increasingly applied to workplace issues in the 1970s. The early work was primarily occupational hygiene, especially related to asbestos services, and these together with laboratory services remained the core of the consultancy business for many years. Jim Dodgson, Head of Environmental Branch who was to become President of the British Occupational Hygiene Society, was key at the outset, initiating the asbestos and occupational hygiene services and building a world-class specialist mineralogical and chemical laboratory capable of dealing with chemical, mineral and fibre samples from most workplaces. He was also an excellent mentor: energetic, enthusiastic, full of ideas and with time for the many young scientists in his branch at the time. Aptly for someone who had been a teacher, coaching in report writing was his speciality. The aim was for clarity and accuracy, and this became the overriding characteristic of IOM reports to clients.

Asbestos control

As knowledge about the harmfulness of asbestos increased and was publicised in the 1960s and 70s, legislation was improved (most importantly, the Asbestos Regulations of 1969), new, better and tighter guidance was issued, and control limits specifically for asbestos were implemented. All these measures, particularly the first of the Health and Safety Executive (HSE) EH10 guidance series. The introduction of asbestos control limits in 1976 greatly expanded the market for services and consultancies. Asbestos was almost ubiquitous in buildings, plant and machinery, and any disturbance during routine operations, maintenance, renovations or demolitions released fibres into the air, resulting in risks to the health of those working there. In the light of public anxiety, many organisations started to remove asbestos which paradoxically put the removal workers and bystanders at potential risk. Standards were not nearly as tight as today's but, by the mid-1970s, employers were removing asbestos from workplaces within enclosures, and air monitoring and clearance surveys were needed before an area could be reoccupied. All this activity required careful control and monitoring and, crucially, expert advice.

The measurement of airborne asbestos fibres is not straightforward. The samples must be collected correctly but the standard method for fibre analysis posed particularly thorny quality problems. The method at the time (and now) is based on optical microscopy using the Walton Beckett eye-piece graticule mentioned in chapter 1.[1] The procedure has several stages, each one of which, from setting up the microscope and correctly preparing the sample to seeing and counting individual fibres, is a potential source of large errors. The Institute used an in-house fibre counting quality scheme, based on particle counting schemes used in earlier PFR research, to maintain analytical quality. The occupational hygienists, laboratory technical staff and colliery investigators were carefully trained in asbestos identification, fibre counting and means of sampling fibres in the air, and were only allowed to count fibres in client samples if they maintained an adequate performance in the scheme. Importantly, this work and the expertise developed led directly to the Regular Interlaboratory Counting Exchanges (RICE) discussed at the end of this chapter.

Much of this work was for large companies and public sector organisations (utilities, local authorities, universities, etc). Sales and marketing activities were minimal, and many clients made contact through other occupational health, hygiene or safety professionals who knew about IOM. The other major user of these services from the 1970s up to independence in 1990 was British Coal, despite having its own in-house capability.

Other work

Other occupational hygiene work was a smaller but important part of the consultancy activity. Most early work related to measurement of airborne contaminants and noise. Dusts and fumes were the mainstay, but organic chemicals, gases and vapours were soon added to the list as the laboratory's analytical capability grew in the 1970s. Contracts were small and largely local to Edinburgh. Measurement of personal exposure to workplace pollutants over a few days at most were the most frequent contracts. Most were stand-alone investigations to assess compliance with the Health and Safety at Work Act of 1974. There were occasional more unusual assignments, one being a contract to measure a crop-spraying pilot's exposure to airborne insecticide in Caithness as part of a complex investigation.

Expansion in the 1980s

Consultancies and services continued to grow during the 1980s. IOM had special expertise in asbestos measurement. In 1981/82 Alec Cowie and Nigel Crawford carried out a review for the European Commission and the Canadian Government to help identify possible improvements in the way that asbestos fibres were evaluated by microscopy.[2] They assessed the possible advantages in modifying the aspect ratio, the ratio of the fibre length to its diameter, used in the evaluation to make the results more relevant to the cancer risk. While the results of this research were positive, the final EU asbestos directive nevertheless standardised the methodologies without making any change to the aspect ratio of the fibres, to maintain some continuity with past epidemiological research.

IOM's office in the North East of England was particularly successful in the provision of asbestos monitoring and related services to industry. The key to success was having the right person at the right time. Alan Bradley had been the senior PFR regional investigator there, working with a small team at Whitburn, near Sunderland. He was given the task of building the consultancy work and he succeeded beyond expectations. He attended and often spoke at local health and safety group meetings, and he and the Institute became well known to the people who recognised potential asbestos problems and influenced the selection of consultants. He made himself known to the local HSE, who added IOM to their list of occupational hygiene and asbestos consultants.

He also gave training lectures which introduced IOM to yet more clients. Bradley was a larger than life character who had enormous energy and enthusiasm. Above all else, he was a practical man who provided solutions, much appreciated by his clients.

The work grew rapidly, and staff from Edinburgh and the remaining Welsh and English Midlands regional offices were regularly called upon to help in NE England. Bradley was moved to Edinburgh in the mid-1980s and transformed the asbestos consultancy there. He was appointed Head of Occupational Hygiene on Dodgson's retirement in 1988. The work not only grew in numbers of contracts but also included larger-scale contracts. One of the first large asbestos monitoring and management contracts undertaken was during asbestos removal on a floating oil storage unit in the North Sea.

In parallel with the growth of the Institute's consultancy work in Edinburgh, the Ergonomics Branch, based in Bretby near Burton-on-Trent in the Midlands, also started to provide consultancy services on a modest scale. Ergonomics services were provided to a diverse mix of industries across the Midlands, including pet food manufacture, potteries and chemical production.

A Passage to India

The first major overseas contract was a direct consequence of IOM's expertise in prevention of dust disease in coal miners. Professor Anthony Seaton, while Director, was contracted by the UK Department for International Development (DID) to advise the nationalised Indian coal industry on preventing pneumoconiosis. This involved teaching the company's many doctors about radiological detection of the disease, teaching the company's engineers about dust measurement in mines, and assisting in setting up a database to record and analyse the results. Dodgson and Dr Brian Miller also took part in this project which occupied three years and involved seven visits to mining areas across India from Bihar to Hyderabad [fig 3.1]. In addition, some thirty Indian

Fig 3.1: Stone workers in India (c.1980)

mine doctors and engineers attended courses on the subject in Edinburgh. Although the project was completed successfully, funding did not become available for a hoped-for audit of the results of this endeavour.

Contaminated land

Even the larger contracts tended to be single discipline and to be quite independent of IOM's research work. A major exception was a contract to manage and monitor asbestos during the demolition and clearance of an asbestos factory. As well as the contamination in the buildings, the surrounding soil was heavily contaminated with asbestos. Clearance of the site and making it fit for reuse posed many questions. Heavily contaminated soil is clearly a potential hazard to health but at what concentrations of asbestos do risks become acceptable? Polarised microscopy was, and still is, used to identify asbestos fibres in bulk materials and it could readily be adapted for soils. In the 1980s, the method's sensitivity was unknown and there was no accepted method of quantifying asbestos in soil. The IOM mineralogist at the time, John Addison, and his team developed and validated an analytical method for quantifying fine asbestos in soil. Large numbers of soil samples were collected and analysed during the clearance work, giving a picture of the nature and extent of contamination. Airborne asbestos fibre monitoring was carried out continuously. Conservative (in terms of health risk) but practical decisions were made for the site, based on the measurements and considerations about how dust is generated. The site was successfully cleared and redeveloped. This consultancy led directly to a research contract with the then UK Department of the Environment to address the issues of quantitative analysis of asbestos in soil, generation of asbestos fibres from contaminated soil, and assessing the associated health risks. The report by Addison and colleagues in 1988 remains a key source of information in assessing risks from asbestos contamination in soils.[3]

Laboratory services

IOM's laboratory under the direction of Dr Alastair Robertson, a chemistry PhD and long-term member of the scientific staff, was a key part of the asbestos work, at the forefront of method

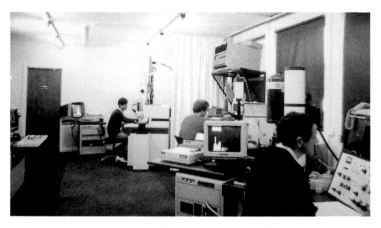

Fig 3.2(a): Scanning Electron Microscope (SEM) Suite,
IOM Roxburgh Place (1980)

Fig 3.2(b): Electron microscopy suite in the IOM building in Riccarton (2005)

development and quality improvement, with staff participating in HSE's asbestos measurement committees. The laboratory was involved in development and refinement of optical and electron microscopy fibre counting, in asbestos analytical techniques for airborne fibres and bulk materials, and in analysis of trace contamination by asbestos in commercial mineral products such as talc and vermiculite [figs 3.2 and 3.3]. Other work

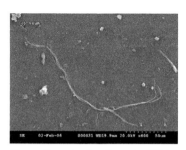

Fig 3.3: Asbestos fibres by scanning electron microscopy

Amosite asbestos

Chrysotile asbestos fibres by SEM

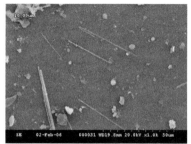

included development of techniques to discriminate between asbestiform and non-asbestiform fibres, both to support research and to facilitate risk assessment for commercial materials.[4] The laboratory gained external accreditation from NAMAS (a predecessor of UKAS)[5] for asbestos analysis in bulk materials and airborne fibre counting in the late 1980s. It was the first part of IOM to achieve this type of national laboratory accreditation, becoming a key building block for the laboratory's future commercial success.

Assessment and control of hazards

Other occupational hygiene work continued to expand through the 1980s. This was given a substantial boost by the COSHH (Control of Substances Hazardous to Health) Regulations and Noise Regulations of 1987 and 1988. Monitoring of hazardous materials and noise, and COSHH risk assessments were common assignments for a wide range of industrial, public and commercial organisations. Some organisations realised that they used hazardous chemicals, for example, for cleaning or printing, only after the regulations came into force. Noise and chemical risks were largely acceptable or close to acceptable in most workplaces but, occasionally, dangerous situations were found. For example, in a large financial organisation's printing press there was extensive slopping about of solvents in an unventilated basement. Also, a worker in the electronics industry, wearing only rubber kitchen gloves, was seen putting his hand into a bath of concentrated hydrofluoric acid to retrieve dropped electronic components. Monitoring also led to improvements. In one example, very high airborne metal fume concentrations were found in a non-ferrous foundry, despite the installation of a new ventilation system over the metal furnace. Further investigation revealed that the new system did not move enough air to match the convection from the furnace, a serious design error by the installers which was soon rectified.

Colin Soutar and Robertson's participation in the Mossmorran and Braefoot Bay Independent Air Quality Monitoring Review Group started in the 1980s. The Mossmorran petrochemical plant is involved in natural gas liquefaction and ethylene production. Raw materials are delivered by gas pipeline to Mossmorran, and the terminal at Braefoot Bay is used to export products. There was considerable local public concern about the possible adverse health effects arising from these operations, and the Review Group was set up by Fife Council to provide advice and recommendations on the monitoring of emissions from the operations at the plants and the terminal facilities. The Review Group, which still meets, consists of an Independent Chair and representatives from Fife Council, the Scottish Environment Protection Agency (SEPA) and IOM. Representatives of the companies involved attend the Review Group meetings by invitation. It liaises with local communities, local community councils and representatives of the local health service. In the earlier years, annual presentations were made to interested local community councils. Independent and impartial IOM experts continue to help this group advise and make recommendations to Fife Council.

New marketing initiatives

By the end of the 1980s, IOM was an established player in the consultancy market. Most of the work was in quite small-scale contracts lasting up to two or three days but several larger, longer-term contracts were won, and a deliberate marketing strategy commenced, using glossy leaflets and promotion of services in local professional societies. IOM's reputation for high quality was known by professionals in the broad field of health at work. The consultancy work had grown remarkably since the 1970s; although in 1990 it remained well below half of the total business of the Institute of Occupational Medicine, it was apparent that there was huge market potential.

Independence: services and consultancies from 1990 to 2005

Marketing and pricing

The services and consultancies business in the new, independent IOM had survived the process of departure from the coal industry almost unscathed, though some reorganisation was required. Most of the work was carried out from the Edinburgh HQ. The office in Nottinghamshire was closed when staff left but small offices were retained near Sunderland and Cardiff. Ergonomics and human factors staff moved to Edinburgh and continued to provide consultancy services from their base in research.

Bolton as Marketing Director increased IOM's profile enormously over the next few years. He put together much more professional information packs and travelled widely throughout the UK and beyond to publicise IOM at many industry and scientific meetings and exhibitions. He encouraged staff to maintain and develop business contacts and to make new contacts among potential customers. His efforts made IOM services much more aware of the marketplace and the marketplace more aware of IOM.

The business grew over the longer term. The type of work did not change but more large-scale contracts were won. Commercial success and development under Soutar's overall leadership were based on the many individuals who had the drive and energy to enthuse staff and customers. There were hiccups, however. In 1992, the asbestos consultancy work virtually dried up, leading to some retrenchment and reorganisation. It transpired that pricing was at the heart of the problem, with new competition undercutting IOM. This was dealt with by some repricing and changing of price structures.

Consultancies in the newly independent IOM

Sheila Groat, a long-term staff member and occupational hygienist, managed asbestos and occupational hygiene from 1992, and there was steady growth. Full surveys of buildings for asbestos materials and requests to manage asbestos removal contracts became more frequent. On the occupational hygiene side, data collected in a series of contracts to measure airborne dust and quartz in Scottish quarries was, unusually, used in research into the respiratory health of quarry workers.[6] One contract, to help manage worker exposures to solvents during tunnelling through contaminated land in a port area, was unusual in both the range and extent of IOM involvement and the difficulty of the situation. Work included breath testing and air monitoring together with advice on respirators and other protective clothing in a hot, high-pressure, highly flammable and restricted environment.

The occupational hygienists, in common with other staff largely assigned to consultancy work, also participated in research. There were clear benefits to both research and consultancy from this: consultancy staff were aware of the latest scientific and technical developments and research benefited from involving practical and highly experienced staff. However, this was becoming more difficult to manage, deadlines being the main problem. Consultancy projects generally lasted a couple of weeks whereas research lasts a year or more. Staff often had several consultancy contracts on the go and, therefore, had to deal with several clients with urgent deadlines, making it difficult to dedicate time to the longer-timescale research work. While a few individuals continued to manage both kinds of work successfully, most individuals specialised in either research or consultancy at a given time. In contrast to occupational hygiene staff, ergonomics and human factors staff were able to continue to provide consultancy and services from their base in research. There was less of a conflict between the two roles, the consultancy deadlines being more flexible, enabling the benefits of the dual role to be retained.

Bradley increased the occupational hygiene expert witness work in Scotland and in the Republic of Ireland, although failure of lawyers to pay bills in the latter country caused this work to cease. Occupational health consultancies also did well under occupational physician Dr Eugene Waclawski, with long-term contracts being won. Dr Alison Searl, who had joined IOM in 1992 as head of the laboratory, started to have a commercial impact quite early with her drive and positive attitude. Much of the work at that time was in Scotland but there were some overseas contracts. Bradley, Seaton (then in Aberdeen) and Robertson undertook an investigation of a zinc and cadmium smelter and the associated opencast mine in Rajasthan. The mine was run relatively safely, but road transport of the ore was unsafe and some of the work in the smelter was extremely so, and recommendations were made to management for improvement. Bradley and Robertson looked at tyre-fuelled electricity generation in the USA in the same year. There were also contracts for work on asbestos in schools in the USA, and asbestos monitoring and management in Azerbaijan.

From their new Edinburgh base, ergonomics and human factors staff, under the leadership of Dr Richard Graveling, provided consultancy services to many of the mainstays of Scottish industry including salmon farming and processing, elements of whisky production and the then burgeoning 'silicon glen' covering aspects of computer and mobile phone manufacture as well as support industries.

Increasing efficiency

John Allan became IOM's Commercial Director and Company Secretary in the mid-1990s. He brought a much harder commercial perspective and a new type of energy to the business. The early relationship was uneasy, but he improved the business at that time, with a focus more on efficiency, utilisation, invoicing and sales. All this prepared the services division well for the big changes that came in around 1997 when the research and consultancy work diverged, and Robertson was appointed Managing Director of Consultancy with a remit to grow the business across the UK.

Fig 3.4: Worker being fitted with an IOM sampler by an IOM occupational
hygienist in a pipe manufacturing facility (2005)

A detailed marketing survey showed results were much better than some had feared. IOM really did have a good position and reputation within the market. The advice was to produce new professional marketing material and to "build it and they shall come", the phrase taken from the popular contemporary film *Field of Dreams*. Section heads wrote short business plans with business aims, products to sell, likely markets and the additional resource that was needed. Gilbert Armstrong, a long-term IOM employee, was transferred from Finance to become headquarters salesperson, an inspired decision, suggested by Allan. The first few months were particularly hard for him. Armstrong visited literally hundreds of current, past and potential clients in that period, up to about ten visits a day. His main aim was to get to know them and make sure that, if they needed work that IOM could provide, they would come to IOM. The work started to trickle in after a few months and then it turned to a steady flow before reaching flood proportions. The Edinburgh consultancy business was transformed. There was substantial growth in the occupational hygiene and asbestos business under Groat and Stuart Goddard [fig 3.4]. Searl and her team dramatically increased laboratory turnover, becoming consistently profitable in the process. Occupational health, by then under Dr Adele Pilkington, Waclawski having emigrated to Canada, was another substantial growth area. Large, long-term contracts were won with several organisations and, at one stage, three occupational health physicians and two occupational health nurse practitioners were employed.

Meanwhile, the ergonomists under Graveling continued to provide their services although, with their continued focus on research, this remained on a relatively small scale in terms of numbers – but not in diversity. The enactment in the early 1990s of the Manual Handling Operations Regulations and the Display Screen Equipment Regulations provided a further driver for their services, the latter finding opportunities *inter alia* in the Edinburgh offices of companies in the banking and insurance sectors.

UK-wide services

The Edinburgh business grew, but the regional business was transformed. The Tyne and Wear office closed when Peter Weston, the NE England asbestos consultant, retired as opportunities for commercially viable work in this area were becoming fewer. A major step forward was taken in 1998, when occupational hygienist Geoff Smith was recruited to build an occupational hygiene business in the Sheffield/Chesterfield area. John Geraghty and Steve Janssen were the next recruits. Janssen was an asbestos consultant and Geraghty was the local salesperson. This team brought immediate success and the office grew rapidly, mainly with asbestos consultancy, a large influx of expert witness work for Smith and some occupational hygiene.

A large consultancy project managing asbestos in tunnels in London was set up by Bradley before he retired. This was run firstly by Mark Lovett (who had transferred from IOM's Cardiff office, which was then closed) and subsequently by Jane Tierney who managed the main asbestos contract very successfully for several years. Eventually an office was opened in Perivale providing asbestos, occupational hygiene and occupational health services for several years. Jerry Slann, a chartered engineer and health and safety professional, was appointed in 2002 to open a West Midlands office near Stafford for asbestos and occupational hygiene consultancies. This office also grew quickly, with a larger proportion of general occupational hygiene work than elsewhere. Notably, he spotted a niche market in hospital operating theatre ventilation testing and he rapidly became, and remains, one of the acknowledged experts in the field. This testing remains a substantial part of IOM's service and consultancy business.

In the 2000s, Robertson was leading an excellent senior team. Quality was addressed by extending UKAS Accreditations to cover almost all laboratory analysis, asbestos sampling and occupational hygiene sampling. Continued compliance was supported by a quality manager, initially Laurie Davies and subsequently Carol MacIntosh. Many new staff were recruited with the help of personnel officer Maureen Quinn. Contract and sales management systems had not kept up with the increased volume of work, but Gordon Outram was recruited as a systems manager in 2004 and made critical project management improvements.

All the offices had many large asbestos contracts over this period. Asbestos legislation and guidance had changed substantially over the years from 1990, driving the asbestos market. The consultancy work was dominated by surveys of asbestos in buildings, associated risk assessments, and asbestos site management during refurbishment and demolition works. Asbestos surveys were carried out in schools, houses, offices, industrial sites, food factories, retail sites, universities, power stations and petrochemical plants. Each type of location raised specific problems. In addition, there were standard surveys, which consisted of inspection and sampling, and destructive surveys which required the surveyor to remove anything which might have been covering asbestos-containing materials, no matter the damage caused.

An example of IOM's capabilities

The largest and probably the most unusual occupational hygiene contract in the 2000s was provision of advice on occupational hygiene and safety advice and a programme of monitoring during the decontamination and demolition of a major electronics plant in Central Scotland. The plant had not been fully cleaned during decommissioning. Thousands of miles of pipework were left and these potentially contained corrosive materials (such as hydrofluoric and nitric acids), toxic and carcinogenic solvents (especially chlorinated hydrocarbons), toxic gases (e.g. hydrogen chloride, chlorine, germane, phosgene), explosive gases (silanes) and a wide range of toxic metals. Asbestos was also a potential issue in some of the older parts of the plant. IOM provided safe procedures, sampled and analysed the contents of all lines and monitored all operations. The whole operation went remarkably smoothly. There were only two incidents in the course of a year-long contract. One sub-contractor received a chemical burn when he tried to steal a contaminated pump from a banned area, and another injured his face slamming his truck door in bad temper after receiving a reprimand from his line manager for a minor safety breach.

Expert witness work

Smith brought substantial new occupational hygiene expert witness work from his Chesterfield office. He passed some out to IOM HQ consultants and actively trained others. In later years, he worked full-time on this, generating substantial income for IOM. Alan Jones developed quantitative asbestos risk assessments. These were linked almost invariably to some sort of incident or situation, either in the general environment or the workplace. He used monitoring data, old and new, and detailed investigations of the situation to estimate individuals' cumulative exposures to asbestos fibres. Contracts for this type of work sometimes expanded to measuring exposures and assessing risk to rural communities from asbestos materials. Examples included the construction of unmetalled country lanes, and assessing asbestos exposures in a cardboard product factory. This contract was complicated by the presence of vast quantities of cardboard fibres and an earlier assumption that all fibres were asbestos. Ergonomics experts such as Graveling, and later Dr Joanne Crawford, provided further support for such services, providing their expertise to solicitors, especially in the field of musculoskeletal disorders.

Environmental consultancies

IOM's environmental consultancy business grew after 2000, primarily under the direction of Searl. As well as the ongoing consultancy for the petrochemical plant, IOM became involved in Environmental Health Impact Assessments and pollution modelling for new major developments, environmental air monitoring and an increasing amount of work on asbestos in soils. The EU's 2007 Regulation, Evaluation, Authorisation and Restriction of Chemicals (REACH) regulations also brought a new area of work for IOM on chemical risk assessment which resulted in substantial ongoing work, both research and consultancy.

One notable contract was IOM's involvement in ascertaining hazard to the population of the island of Montserrat in the West Indies from dust inhalation following the massive volcanic eruption of 1995, when a pyroclastic flow had buried the capital of the island in dust; this work involved extensive dust sampling and analysis and medical and radiological surveys, and led to research publications initially on the nature of the dust and the magnitude of islanders' exposures to it.[7, 8]

Regular Interlaboratory Counting Exchanges

IOM developed and then managed the Regular Interlaboratory Counting Exchanges (RICE) on behalf of HSE for over twenty years, a totally different service from any other provided by IOM.

RICE and IOM had an enormous impact on the quality of fibre counting by phase contrast microscopy in the UK, with dramatic improvements being made and maintained. Airborne asbestos concentrations have been measured for many years by drawing air through membrane filters which are mounted on glass slides and cleared (made transparent) prior to fibre counting by phase contrast optical microscopy (PCOM). Large errors can arise at every stage. The method requires skilled and careful technicians, good and well-maintained equipment and standard, systematic methodology. In 1978, HSE's Advisory Committee on Asbestos recommended that laboratories engaged in evaluating fibre concentrations using PCOM should accept the need to adopt regular check counting procedures both within and between laboratories to ensure good quality control.[9] RICE arose out of this recommendation.

RICE was much more than a proficiency testing scheme. In the 1970s, there were no standard membrane filter evaluation methods. Different laboratories used different sampling procedures and different filter mounting methods. There was no standard microscope specification, the microscope set-up and magnification differed between laboratories, and there was no accepted procedure for testing microscope set-up. Moreover, several different fibre counting methods and rules were routinely used. The Central Reference Scheme (CRS) had been set up in 1978, with IOM having the key role of the Central Reference Laboratory. The CRS prepared the way for the RICE scheme.

The CRS and IOM determined the impacts of different methodologies on results, assessed differences between experienced laboratories, investigated the effects of training and standardised fibre counting methods. Three grades of fibre counting performance standard for participating laboratories were defined. There were no reference samples for a quality scheme at the outset and potential reference slides were collected and assessed by IOM. The CRS demonstrated that the Magiscan automatic image analyser (Joyce-Loebl) with the Manchester Asbestos Program (MAP) was a good source of reference fibre counts for these stock samples.[10]

RICE was managed by IOM for over twenty years. Crawford, then Jones (both PhD graduates) and Patrick Brown were the key personnel. Following a seminar for participants, the first formal round of RICE took place in 1984.[11] Initial results were quite shocking. A hundred and seventy-five laboratories participated and fifty of them were in the worst performance category after the first round. Systematic differences of up to 150-fold occurred between mean laboratory counts, with 300-fold differences being found for individual samples.[12]

RICE was supported by a National Training Programme and many of the poorer-performing laboratories took advantage of this. Laboratories sought advice from IOM. Internal exchanges were set up, microscopes realigned, counting procedures changed and internal quality audits undertaken. Substantial improvements in fibre counting quality arose immediately. In the second round of RICE, only six laboratories were in the worst performance category and the number in the top performance category increased from 77 to 125. The HSE/NPL test slide was introduced in the 1980s and this greatly helped laboratories set up microscopes consistently.[13] Performance improved through the 1980s and 90s.[12,14] RICE was refined and improved over the years. Low-density samples were included from 1992. Manual reference fibre counts were adopted at the same time for all reference samples. New performance criteria for the low-density slides were developed and adopted, and circulations were designed to avoid bias from the circulation of different numbers of low- and high-density slides.

RICE, under IOM management and with IOM expertise, became a smooth-running and effective proficiency testing scheme for asbestos fibre counting. Reference samples were relevant to the everyday work of the participating laboratories. Acceptable performance criteria were in place. IOM and RICE had prompted huge improvements in fibre counting quality assurance and had truly made a difference. However, HSE decided to take RICE in-house in 2005.

IOM now runs a much smaller, international quality assurance scheme (Asbestos Fibre Regular Informal Counting Arrangement (AFRICA)). The operation of this scheme follows similar principles to RICE,[11,12] except that there are no formal criteria of acceptability nor is there a supporting training scheme. As with RICE, the AFRICA scheme has also seen substantial improvements in fibre counting quality control.[14]

Consultancy in 2005

The period from 1990 to 2005 was one of considerable growth in the services component of IOM's business, and consolidation of the rapid growth was hard work. When Soutar retired in 2005 and Dr Phil Woodhead took over as Chief Executive, Consultancy was in good shape. In 2005/06, the last year before restructuring, Consultancy income exceeded £5 million, which was over three quarters of the total IOM business. IOM Headquarters was thriving, with three well-established regional offices, and prospects were good.

Chapter 3: References and Notes

1. Walton WH, Beckett ST. (1977). A microscope eye-piece graticule for the evaluation of fibrous dust. *Annals of Occupational Hygiene*; 20:19-23.

2. Cowie AJ, Crawford NP. (1982). A comparison of the effects of different counting rules and aspect ratios on the level and reproducibility of asbestos fibre counts. Part 1: Effects on level. Final report on CEC Contract 'Counting rules for asbestos fibre measurements at work'. Edinburgh: Institute of Occupational Medicine. (IOM Report TM/82/23).

3. Addison J, Davies LST, Robertson A, Willey RJ. (1988). The release of dispersed asbestos from soils. Edinburgh: Institute of Occupational Medicine. (IOM Report TM/88/14).
4. Langer AM, Nolan RP, Addison J. (1991). Distinguishing between amphibole asbestos and elongated cleavage fragments of their non-asbestos analogues. In: Brown RC, Hoskins JA, Johnson NF, eds. *NATO Advanced Research Workshop on Mechanisms in Fibre Carcinogenesis*. New York: Plenum Press.
5. United Kingdom Accreditation Service (UKAS). https://www.ukas.com/
6. Love RG, Agius RM, Cowie HA, Davies LST, Hurley JF. (1993). Radiological abnormalities and personal dust exposure among hard rock quarry workers. In: Hurych J, Lesage M, David A, eds. Eighth International Conference on Occupational Lung Diseases, 14-17 September 1992, Prague, Czechoslovakia. Proceedings. Vols. 1-3. Geneva: International Labour Office: 664-676.
7. Searl A, Nicholl A, Baxter PJ. (2002). Assessment of the exposure of islanders to ash from the Soufrière Hills volcano, Montserrat, British West Indies. *Occupational and Environmental Medicine*; 59: 523-531.
8. Baxter PJ, Bonadonna C, Dupree R, Hards VL, Kohn SC, Murphy MD, Nichol A, Nicholson RA, Norton G, Searl A, Sparks RSJ, Vickers BP. (1999). Cristobalite in volcanic ash of the Soufrière Hills Volcano, Montserrat, British West Indies. *Science*; 283: 1142-1145.
9. HSC Advisory Committee on Asbestos. (1978). Second Report – measurement and monitoring of asbestos in air. London: Health and Safety Commission.
10. Dixon RN. (1982). Recent comparison of Magiscan with manual counters. In: Proceedings of the Fourth International Colloquium on Dust Measuring Technique and Strategy. Edinburgh, 20-23 September 1982. London: Asbestos International Association: 113-132.

11. Crawford NP, Cowie AJ. (1984). Quality control of airborne asbestos fibre counts in the United Kingdom – the present position. *Annals of Occupational Hygiene*: 28: 391-398.

12. Crawford NP, Brown P, Cowie AJ. (1992). The RICE and AFRICA schemes for asbestos fibre counting. *Annals of Occupational Hygiene*; 36: 59-69.

13. Le Guen JMM, Ogden TL, Shenton-Taylor T, Verrill JF. (1984). The HSE/NPL phase-contrast test slide. *Annals of Occupational Hygiene*; 28: 237-247.

14. Brown PW, Jones AD, Miller BG. (2002). Developments in the RICE Asbestos Fibre Counting Scheme, 1992-2000. *Annals of Occupational Hygiene*; 46: 329-339.

4

Changing with the times: 2005 to 2019

Summary

The period from early 2005 onwards began with the arrival of Dr Philip Woodhead as Chief Executive following the retirement of Dr Colin Soutar. Thus began a period of evolution rather than revolution, building on some excellent foundations. Nevertheless, it was also a period of much change, with increasing emphasis on commercial development of consultancies and services. The funding landscape for IOM's research activities underwent a considerable shift, with UK funding diminishing markedly, and European funding growing in importance in its place, particularly for research into the new nanotechnologies and related safety issues. IOM became a leading player in Europe into collaborative research related to safety of nano-sized materials. Three years into this period came one of the deepest recessions in living memory, and although there was no immediate impact on IOM's business, the effects were increasingly felt in the longer term, as most of the markets IOM operated in became more competitive and price-sensitive. This was primarily a consequence of the squeeze on public sector finances, and the knock-on effect into other sectors. Organisationally, the composition of IOM's Board of Governors changed completely during this period, and the membership of the executive management team also underwent many changes. New services were developed, some established services were discontinued, and IOM successfully opened its first overseas office in Singapore. The expertise of the senior scientists in its new location close to Heriot Watt University was recognised by the university appointing four of them honorary professors.

A change of chief executive

In February 2005, Dr Philip Woodhead was appointed as CEO [fig 4.1]. He had previously pursued a career in the pharmaceutical industry, first with Glaxo, and latterly with the leading pharmaceutical services company Quintiles Transnational, where he was Vice President, Pharmaceutical Sciences (Europe). All previous heads of IOM had been medical doctors with a background in occupational research, so it would be fair to say that Woodhead's appointment was a break with tradition and a bold move by the Governors. They clearly felt that IOM was already sufficiently strong in its own traditional areas of scientific endeavour, and that the appointment of someone with experience of managing a growing business in a science-based service industry would be complementary to IOM's established scientific strengths.

Fig 4.1: Dr Phil Woodhead, Chief Executive 2005-16

Management structures and processes as of 2005

At the time of Woodhead's appointment, the company structure was well established (IOM parent, with charitable status, and IOM Consulting as a wholly owned subsidiary). Any profits made by the subsidiary were to be gift-aided to the charity. A Board of Governors was in place, having been formed in 1990 upon IOM gaining full independence from British Coal, and comprised Professor Russel Griggs OBE (Chair), Sir Frank Davies and Professor Philip Love CBE. The Chief Executive and the Company Secretary were expected to attend Governors' meetings, which typically took place three times a year. A Board of Management was also in place, comprising an executive management team and a non-executive Chair (also Professor Griggs, the Chair of Governors). The majority of the members of this Board were senior scientists from across the company, and most were also divisional heads. This Board met quarterly.

A divisional structure was in place, reflecting the company structure, with Research under Fintan Hurley as the domain of the charity, and Consultancy under Dr Alastair Robertson as the domain of IOM Consulting. Subsidiary Boards had been established to manage the affairs of Research and Consultancy respectively. All business support functions were grouped together in a third separate division, managed by John Allan. A Special Projects division had also been established as a means to develop new research themes, and this initiative was led by Dr John Cherrie, a physics graduate who had completed a PhD on exposure assessment at Aberdeen University and was to become Research Director and later a professor at Heriot Watt University. At the time of Woodhead's appointment, the role of Scientific Director was created, to oversee the integrity and rigour of the science practised within IOM. Fintan Hurley was appointed to this role, alongside his responsibilities as Research Director. The Consultancy activities comprised (in the main) Asbestos Consultancy, Occupational Hygiene Services, Occupational Health Services, and Analytical (Laboratory) Services. Where a section undertook both research and consultancy work (for example Ergonomics and Human Factors), its positioning within one division or another tended to be determined by the major part of its work and the leanings of the senior staff managing the section. Two separate committees had been established to facilitate consultation between management and staff. One of these, the Joint Review Council, was concerned largely with pay and conditions. The other (the Consultative Committee) allowed for consultation on any other matter judged as relevant. Both these groups were chaired by the Chief Executive.

The company was headquartered in Edinburgh, having moved from the centre of Edinburgh to bespoke new premises on the Heriot Watt Research Park in November 2003 including purpose-built laboratories. There were regional offices in Chesterfield, Stafford and London; these provided greater geographical reach for IOM Consulting, and had no role in IOM's research activities. All staff were jointly employed by IOM and IOM Consulting for contractual purposes, although individual staff were in practice aligned with one group company or the other.

A formal quality system underpinned many of the services offered by IOM Consulting, and was subject to external audit by UKAS. The company had a clear mission statement: "*to benefit those at work and in the community by providing quality research, consultancy and training in health, hygiene and safety and by maintaining our independent impartial position as an international centre of excellence*". The values enshrined in this statement, i.e. independence, impartiality, quality and excellence, seemed to be well understood and embraced by staff. In the financial year 2004-05, more than 70% of the turnover of the company had been attributable to IOM Consulting.

Organisational changes as the period unfolded

The Board of Governors was progressively expanded from three to six, and the original members eventually stood down.

At the close of Woodhead's tenure as CEO, the Governors were: Margaret Burns CBE, a lawyer and former Health and Safety Commissioner (Chair); Alastair Atkinson, CEO of DySIS, a Scottish medical diagnostics company; Stephen Hutt, Chief Financial Officer at Green Highland Renewables, Professor Susan Deacon, former Scottish Minister of Health; Liz Mallinson, British Telecom's Commercial Director of Next Generation Access Scotland, and Ray Jones, Director of the Scottish Agricultural Organisations Society. This was clear evidence that IOM continued to attract people of the highest calibre to serve as Governors.

The Boards of Management and Governors continued to meet on a quarterly basis throughout the period, and a Senior Management Team, comprising the executive members of the Board of Management, met monthly. The two consultative committees were combined into one, to be known as the Staff Council. Its remit was to allow consultation on any matter associated with working at IOM, and as far as possible, all functions and locations within the organisation were represented.

Early in the period covered by this chapter, Allan retired, and Chris Owens, a chartered accountant who had worked under Allan as Financial Controller, became the new Finance Director. For a time, the remaining business support functions – HR, IT and Secretarial Services – reported directly to the CEO, but later were placed under Owens' management, to be followed by Marketing, thus recognising Owens' increasingly important contribution, as Director of Central Services, to the business.

Research funding

Two events of great significance to IOM's research business unfolded in the period 2004-06. The first was the 2004 UK Royal Society and Royal Academy of Engineering's report on nanoscience and nanotechnology, which pointed to both the opportunities and, also, the possible hazards of the exploitation of this science. Over time, its recognition of the possibility of human and environmental risks raised questions that led to many research opportunities for IOM. The second, with very different implications for IOM, was an abrupt decision in 2006 by the Health and Safety Executive to cut externally contracted research to an absolute minimum and wherever possible to place future research projects at their own Health and Safety Laboratory in Buxton. This was a major blow, given that HSE had previously been one of the most important supporters of IOM's research. It also led to the summary withdrawal from IOM of the RICE scheme which, as mentioned in chapter 3, IOM had developed and managed with great distinction for twenty years.

Nanosafety

Research funding from UK Government bodies progressively declined throughout the period. This was, however, compensated for by increased funding won from the European Commission's Framework Programmes, especially from the extraordinary efforts of Dr Lang Tran (see chapter 9). Most, though not all, of IOM's funding from these programmes related to the safety of nanomaterials. In 2006, principally through the efforts of Dr Rob Aitken, IOM secured substantial funding from the (then) Technology Strategy Board, part of the Department of Trade and Industry, and from Scottish Enterprise, to facilitate the creation of a centre of excellence in nanomaterial safety (SAFENANO). Its purpose was initially to collect and provide guidance on good practice, and subsequently to provide services on toxicology, exposure and risk management for industry and government. In 2009, Steve Hankin, a PhD chemist with a good knowledge of toxicology, who had recently joined IOM from Health Protection Scotland, was appointed Operations Director specifically to lead and develop the SAFENANO team under Aitken's direction.

As IOM developed a programme of fundamental research in nanomaterial safety, SAFENANO forged a role helping innovator companies to undertake product development in a safe and responsible manner, paying due regard to workers' health, consumers' health and environmental consequences. IOM collaborated in this manner with companies from a broad spectrum of different industries, on innovation-led projects funded by the European Communities' FP7 and Horizon 2020 research programmes.

Exposure and other research

Other major areas of research during this period, described in the following chapters, included exposure research and the exposome; exposure modelling; epidemiological studies; the burden of disease, especially cancer; methodological developments for population health impact assessment; air quality studies and the impact of pollution on life expectancy; and environmental determinants of public health specifically in Scotland. Towards the end of the period, IOM had begun to get involved also in citizen science as a means of collecting research data. In addition to conducting original research, the Research division continued its long tradition of developing and revising guidance on behalf of governments and regulatory agencies.

Senior appointments and the creation of the Consulting and Reviews division

The divisional structure was modified during 2006 to allow the creation of a third operational division, to be known as Consulting and Reviews. This had roots in both IOM and IOM Consulting. Aitken was appointed to lead this new division, and the SAFENANO team was incorporated, thus providing continuity in the leadership of IOM's nanotechnology initiative. At the same time, Cherrie was appointed Research Director, allowing Hurley to focus on his Scientific Director responsibilities and his research interests within Environment and Health. Dr Martie van Tongeren, holder of a PhD in Occupational Health, then a senior lecturer at Manchester

University, was recruited to head the Exposure section and to lead the research development effort within Research division. This was a key appointment, leading ultimately to his being appointed Research Director when Cherrie chose to stand down; Hilary Cowie then took a more prominent role as Director of Research Operations.

Expert witness work

One of the intended consequences of creating the Consulting and Reviews division was to collect together much of the higher-value consultancy work being undertaken within IOM, and to distinguish it from more routine service provision. Over time, this proved particularly successful in relation to expert witness work, which had hitherto been undertaken sporadically and had been taken on by any of a handful of senior scientists when it could be fitted in alongside other commitments. During the period in question, an increasing number of experienced IOM scientists became focused either solely or predominantly on this kind of work, so that IOM latterly became one of the leading UK providers of expert witnesses to industrial disease cases. Most cases concerned asbestos-related diseases, other occupational cancers and musculoskeletal disorders. Some of these same scientists were also able to offer complex retrospective risk assessments in cases of putative asbestos exposure. A notable exponent of this kind of work was Dr Alan Jones, another long-time employee and former senior research scientist. The group was managed from the Chesterfield office, initially by Geoff Smith and latterly by Andy Stelling, both experienced occupational hygienists of considerable standing, and both recruited by Robertson. Smith had originally been recruited to manage Consultancy activities in the regional offices and was already well established in expert witness work. Stelling had been recruited from the multinational environmental consultancy RPS Group to head up the Chesterfield office, which for the most part meant managing the Asbestos section there. Stelling subsequently made a great success of transitioning into expert witness work. The group grew under Stelling's leadership, and adopted a mixed employment model, with self-employed associates working alongside permanent IOM employees.

Centre for Health Impact Assessment

IOM established a dedicated Centre for Health Impact Assessment (HIA) within the Consulting and Reviews division, with recruitment to its London Office of Dr Salim Vohra, an established and able practitioner of health impact assessment. This group carried out a wide range of environment-related practical HIA projects, sometimes involving Edinburgh staff, notably Hurley, Cowie and Searl. The Edinburgh team also carried out a range of smaller projects, led by Searl and Cowie, for NHS Health Scotland and for SEPA, the Scottish Environmental Protection Agency. Despite several significant projects and associated publications, it was not possible to grow the London-led HIA work and the initiative was allowed to lapse when Vohra left to set up a small independent consultancy.

The changing fortunes of IOM Services

The more routine activities of what had always been termed 'Consultancy' now became known as 'Services'. These services continued under Robertson's leadership until 2008, when he stood down from his Director position. They then became separate divisions in their own right, reporting to the Chief Executive. These services were essentially the backbone of IOM Consulting's operations, and were expected to be generators of profit, thereby providing a buffer for the expected periods of ebb and flow in research funding. Life, as it turned out, was not always that simple.

Asbestos Services

Asbestos Services had for many years been IOM's largest discrete business entity, both in terms of numbers of staff employed and turnover generated. Throughout 2005-16, IOM had Asbestos teams in all four UK offices, and during that time, it was accorded divisional status, initially under Stuart Goddard, who had joined IOM in the early 1980s from school on the Government's Youth Training Scheme. He had gradually worked his way up through increasingly senior roles, and successfully managed the Edinburgh Asbestos section for several years prior to his appointment as division head. More recently, the division was headed up by John Toms, who had pursued a career as a loss adjuster before managing an asbestos removal and consultancy organisation in the west of Scotland.

It was, however, a turbulent part of the business, characterised by some strong trading and some very difficult periods. It operated in a market undergoing a gradual contraction, having already passed its peak, becoming increasingly price-sensitive and, arguably, commoditised. IOM was widely recognised as a leader, with a strong focus on quality, and with highly competent and professional staff, but was often unsuccessful when competing for business with lower-cost competitors. The company nevertheless maintained strong business relationships with certain customer groups such as universities, local authorities and managing agents for commercial property.

Occupational Hygiene Services

Occupational Hygiene Services operated from the Edinburgh and Stafford offices, under Sheila Groat and Jerry Slann respectively. Groat was an experienced occupational hygienist and long-term IOM employee, and Slann was a chartered engineer and former manager at British Coal. Occupational Hygiene operated initially as two distinct sections within Consultancy division, and later as a division in its own right. For a brief period, the division was led by Chris Beach, a senior hygienist who had been recruited from Transport for London specifically to create and build an Occupational Hygiene section at the London office. This venture failed to gain the necessary traction and, after Beach left, Slann was appointed division head.

Here again, IOM's quality, professionalism and technical leadership were widely recognised, not least in a long-term relationship with the Environment Agency, to whom IOM provided a wide range of services, including strategic advice. However, maintaining high staff utilisation and hence profitability was not always straightforward. Industrial customers would often postpone occupational hygiene surveys or sampling programmes at short notice when their manufacturing schedules took priority. There was also a gradual trend away from physical measurement in some industrial sectors, towards paper risk assessments; to some extent this was encouraged by the regulatory climate in the UK.

Hospital Ventilation Services

In parallel with these trends, IOM had developed a successful Hospital Ventilation Service, largely through the efforts of Slann and his team in the Stafford office. This began as a by-product of IOM's established occupational hygiene capability (particularly in local exhaust ventilation testing), but rapidly became a substantial service in its own right, provided almost exclusively from the Stafford office. This service aims to ensure that critical ventilation systems within the hospital environment function according to specification in relation to airflows, pressure cascades, and microbiological and particulate quality. This applies to operating theatres, catheter laboratories, sterile service departments, radiopharmacy units and indeed any facilities where the control of airflow and air quality is critical, either for containment purposes, or for ensuring that clean room conditions are maintained [fig 4.2]. It is worth noting that this service is an integral part of infection control within the hospital environment and is therefore delivered in the interests of both public and employees' health. IOM gradually established a strong market presence, particularly in England. It was possible to offer a nationwide rather than just a local service, travel time and cost proving to be much less of a barrier than in the other services.

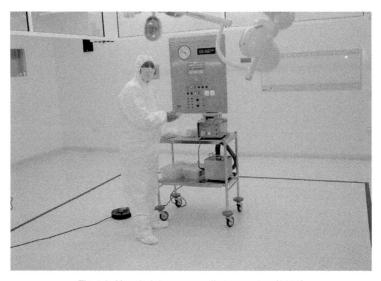

Fig 4.2: Hospital theatre ventilation testing (2010)

It did, however, lead IOM to offer a variation on its standard terms and conditions of employment, given that much of this work is of necessity carried out in the evenings and at weekends in order to minimise downtime in hospital operating theatres and other critical healthcare facilities.

Occupational Health Services

IOM had historically been able to attract a succession of consultant occupational health physicians who were interested both in participating in research and in providing a commercial occupational health service to industrial and public sector clients. Dr Trevor Cattermole, an occupational physician with experience as far afield as the British Antarctic Survey, was effectively the last of this line. Eventually, this hybrid arrangement subsided, and Cattermole was succeeded initially by Dr Lisa Birrell, who joined from Rolls-Royce in East Kilbride. From this point onwards, Occupational Health focused more exclusively on the provision of a clinical occupational health service to employers. Historically this service had always been delivered from the Edinburgh office but, in an effort to grow the business, a second office was opened in London, and Dr James Preston, an occupational physician with experience at BUPA, was recruited to lead the initiative. The new team enjoyed early success, primarily through substantial work over several years for one of the UK's largest civil engineering contractors, resulting in the provision of service during the construction phases of the 2012 London Olympics and of Crossrail. At the same time, some long-term clients at the Edinburgh office were lost, Birrell left, and the department was consolidated at the London office. An occupational health manager, Keith Heywood, was recruited, so clinicians could concentrate on clinical work rather than the commercial side. Heywood's original professional training was in law, but he had gained considerable occupational health management experience. This management model became firmly established following Preston's departure and the arrival of Dr Kirsti Ereneva as consultant physician. Some other notable contracts were secured, particularly in the higher education sector. However, the department was unable to achieve sufficient growth or consistent profitability, and the business was ultimately divested.

Analytical Services

IOM's Analytical (Laboratory) Services division was a model of consistency and financial stability throughout the period in question. This was and is an occupational hygiene laboratory, with sub-sections dedicated to Chemistry, Mineralogy and Protective Suit Testing. For most of this period, the division was led by Dr Alison Searl, with particularly notable support from Steve Clark and Carolyn McGonagle. Searl maintained a lifelong interest in bird life, and this eventually led to her decision to leave IOM and take up employment with the RSPB in the north east of Scotland. Following her departure, the division was incorporated into a bigger grouping, including SAFENANO, under the leadership of Hankin.

The management and staff of this division had over many years earned a reputation for quality, technical expertise, rigorous attention to detail and not a little creativity when it came to trying to measure the almost unmeasurable. Consequently, although the division always had the shortest order book in the company, it routinely turned in the strongest financial performance. Much, though not all, of Mineralogy's work involved analysing for the presence of asbestos, either in bulk building materials or in soil samples [fig 4.3]. During the period covered by this chapter, there was a surge in demand for the testing of soil samples for the presence of asbestos. The most notable example was an extensive programme of work for Wolverhampton Borough Council, analysing soil samples taken from domestic gardens on a large housing estate that had been constructed on the site of a former Courtauld's factory. This large project extended well beyond laboratory testing, to health risk assessment and the provision of guidance to the Council. It was managed by Robertson and Jones, employing a sampling strategy devised by Jones and Cowie.

Fig 4.3: Analysis of bulk asbestos,
part of the Mineralogy laboratory, IOM Riccarton (2005)

The work of the Chemistry section generally involved the analysis of samples collected in the workplace, on swabs, wipes or filters, using conventional chromatographic and spectroscopic techniques [fig 4.4]. Suit testing was carried out on behalf of several leading protective suit manufacturers, to assess resistance to penetration by liquids and dusts, and to assess compliance with certified standards. There was an attempt early in the period in question to add some immunological tests (animal allergens; endotoxin) to the range of laboratory services offered. This was abandoned when it was found that the methods could not be validated with the rigour required for a commercial service offering. Throughout, the financial performance of the division was significantly bolstered by Searl's many and varied consultancy activities.

The opening of the first overseas office

In 2011 exploratory discussions were held with a variety of agencies in Singapore, and after two fact-finding visits to the country, the momentous decision was taken to open an IOM office

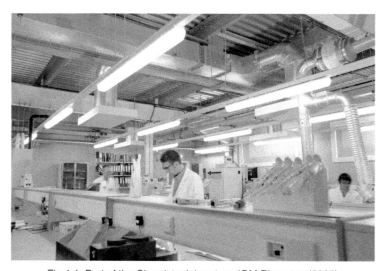

Fig 4.4: Part of the Chemistry laboratory, IOM Riccarton (2005)

there. This was to be IOM's first overseas operation. The rationale for doing this was founded on three main premises. Firstly, that IOM's expertise in safety of nanomaterials was of great interest to the Singapore Government's Economic Development Board (EDB). Secondly, that the Singapore Government seemed intent on raising the bar in relation to workplace safety and health, and had clearly stated their intention to embrace best practice in this regard, as established in the UK and other western countries. They therefore seemed receptive to help from experienced practitioners such as IOM, providing such practitioners were willing to establish a physical presence in the country. Thirdly, that a presence in Singapore would be a staging post for further expansion in Asia where it was clear that there was a great need for IOM's expertise to improve the prevailing working conditions.

With the benefit of a grant from the Singapore EDB, negotiated by Woodhead and Aitken, IOM opened an office in Raffles Place, Singapore in September 2012 and IOM Singapore was born. Aitken relocated to become the first Managing Director. Robertson, who had previously been Director of Services, was seconded for an initial period of three months to help establish the business. Dr Michael Riediker, an exposure scientist from IST (Institut de Santé au Travail) in Lausanne, who had previously collaborated with Aitken on several EU projects, was recruited to lead the nanomaterial safety activity. Zephan Chan, a Singaporean occupational hygienist and safety professional, joined shortly afterwards. The initial hope was that two distinct services could be established, one in the highly specialised field of nanomaterial safety, the other in the broader field of traditional occupational hygiene. It was felt that both of these services could be of legitimate value and interest to industry and government. Over the next four years, the shape of the business changed numerous times. Forging a business based on advising industry on nanomaterial safety proved very challenging, and this did not take off as well or as quickly as expected. Occupational hygiene also developed slowly, but in time a number of good industrial clients were acquired, and this service was doing well as the period was drawing to a close. In 2015, IOM Singapore acquired the business and staff of a small consultancy, Soma Pte, which added further capability and industrial clients. After a couple of years, management took the view that there was an opportunity to create a training business centred on workplace safety and health. Numerous courses were created, and many external accreditations gained from bodies such as IOSH and BOHS. Training thus became a mainstay of the Singapore office's day-to-day operations.

Somewhat unexpectedly, IOM also managed to establish a research capability in Singapore, and from quite early on was able to compete for and secure substantial research funding from the Government. The funded studies spanned nanomaterial safety in workplaces and in the water supply, and the burden of disease

Fig 4.5: IOM Singapore staff in Raffles Place, Singapore, outside Chevron House, the location of IOM's first office (2014)

within the construction sector. At its peak in early 2016, IOM Singapore had ten staff [fig 4.5]. It has declined a little since, but it remains a viable and vibrant business with clients across SE Asia, with excellent prospects for growth.

New approaches to marketing IOM

Back in the UK, changes were occurring in the way IOM sold and marketed its services. In 2005, IOM had a functional website describing its services and other activities, and occasionally produced a hard copy newsletter. Research staff demonstrated their capabilities in the traditional way by publishing papers, presenting at conferences and through peer-to-peer networking. Within Consultancy, a number of full-time sales people were employed and were incentivised to go out and win new business, either from new or established clients. Over time, the company's belief in the salesperson model of business development waned, to the extent that eventually all of the salespeople were let go. The onus then transferred to operational staff, particularly senior staff, to work at the interface with customers, not just from an operational perspective, but also from a business development perspective. This expectation was placed on staff right across the business, in research and consulting as well as in services. Naturally, some staff took to this better than others. To help with this transition, however, a conscious decision was made when recruiting senior staff (particularly division heads), to prioritise business acumen and entrepreneurial skills as well as scientific and technical expertise, so that the successful candidates might lead by example when it came to developing new business.

In parallel with these changes, a marketing director, Grant Law, was recruited and was subsequently invited to join the Board of Management. Law brought considerable experience of digital marketing, principally from within the IT industry where he had held senior positions in major corporations. As a consequence of this appointment, marketing and communications were placed on a

Fig 4.6: IOM Exhibition marketing

much more professional footing, digital marketing was much more to the fore through a strengthened online presence, and more use was made of the rapidly advancing phenomenon of social as well as traditional media [fig 4.6].

Academic recognition

Several senior scientists in the past had been appointed to academic chairs after leaving the Institute, but after the move to Heriot Watt Research Park, that university recognised the research expertise of a number of current staff in 2012 by appointing Hurley, Cherrie, Aitken and Tran as honorary professors.

A further change at the helm

In November 2016, Woodhead retired as Chief Executive and was replaced by Aitken who returned from Singapore to take up the role [fig 4.7]. At the time of Aitken's appointment, several new challenges were emerging.

Fig 4.7: Dr Rob Aitken, Chief Executive 2016 to date

As referred to above, increasingly difficult trading conditions and continued difficulties in the financial performance of the Asbestos division had resulted in a depletion of IOM's cash reserves, and stringent procedures for the management of cash flow had already been introduced. In addition, the order book for Research had declined substantially and the prospect of Brexit threatened access to European research funding going forward. One of Aitken's first tasks was to complete the divestment of the asbestos business, a process that had been initiated by his predecessor. In looking to find a safe home for this business and the staff within it, negotiations were entered into with several companies. Ultimately, the successful bidder was a company which, at the time, was judged to provide the best fit with IOM's values and ethos. The divestment involved the transfer of thirty-five staff to the new company and so was a significant change in the size and shape of IOM. Although traumatic, it was widely recognised that this was the best possible solution both for the transferring staff and for the remainder of IOM, and in that regard could be considered a success.

In early 2017 Aitken recruited Dr Sotiris Vardoulakis as Research Director, to replace van Tongeren, who had decided to return to the University of Manchester, having been offered the position of Professor of Occupational and Environmental Health to succeed another previous IOM employee, Professor Raymond Agius. A physicist with a background in exposure science, Vardoulakis had over twenty years' experience in air pollution, climate change and environmental health research, policy and practice. Previously he was Head of the Environmental Change Department, and Leader of the Air Pollution and Climate Change Group at Public Health England. Through Vardoulakis and Dr Miranda Loh, another environmental scientist who had joined IOM a few years earlier, IOM significantly expanded its research activity in air pollution, sustainability public health and the new urban agenda. By 2018, IOM led one and was a partner in two further international air pollution projects working with partners in Beijing, Bangkok and Delhi.

Aitken, working with Law, imported the model developed in Singapore to launch Training as a new business stream for IOM in the UK. This brought together various *ad hoc* training activities which had been delivered over the years and put them on a proper business footing, with course development, quality control, accreditation and marketing.

Further changes occurred in the senior team around that time. Hurley retired from the position of Scientific Director after more than forty years' distinguished service to IOM. Law moved on to other employment, and a new marketing manager, Aimee Mcintosh, was recruited from Guardian News International. A new more strategic full-time HR manager role was created and Michelle Reid, an HR professional with a background in retail, was recruited.

A new business strategy was developed to build on these changes and to drive further change, particularly in culture, through the organisation. IOM 2018-2023, A Strategy for Success, launched in 2018, redefined and clarified IOM's purpose and values and defined three strategic aims around science, people and finance. At the heart of this strategy was a programme of people-centred change to drive engagement and innovation through all aspects of the business, and to reshape IOM into a more robust, innovative and successful organisation fit to set out on its journey over the next fifty years of its life. The success or otherwise of this strategy will be judged by others over the next few years.

Part 2

The Scientific Contributions

5

Population studies: contributions to occupational and environmental epidemiology

Summary

IOM was set up in 1969 to continue the Pneumoconiosis Field Research (PFR), the nationalised coal industry's major research programme on coal miners' lung disease, and this was IOM's central activity for many years. The PFR was an epidemiological study, i.e. a direct investigation of (i) miners' exposures to airborne coal mine dust, (ii) the health of the lungs, and (iii) the relationships between them.

In a series of publications through the 1970s and 80s, and to a lesser extent later, IOM research clarified the key relationships. Miners' exposure to airborne mixed coal mine dust, rather than to quartz, was the best predictor of pneumoconiosis; the resulting exposure-response relationship provided the scientific basis for dust standards in coalmines in the UK, USA, Germany and other countries. Quartz in unusually high concentrations, for example when cutting stone in roof and floor, had an important subsidiary role. Smoking is a cause of chronic obstructive lung disease (COPD) in miners, but so also is coal dust exposure, independently of smoking. Studies of coal miners' causes of death showed in general no excess of lung cancer, though recent findings have suggested a relationship with quartz in coal mine dust.

Increasingly, the experience and reputation in epidemiology gained by IOM through the PFR was used in other industries – steel,

PVC, fibres, brickworks, quarries, opencast coal, wool, and others; then with a wider range of occupational risks – pesticides, back pain, keyboard work. In the early 1990s the research extended also to outdoor air pollution and other environmental and health issues, especially notable contributions being made to understanding the impacts of environmental pollution on the health and mortality of populations.

This chapter therefore tells two linked stories. One is how, over time, IOM extended its capability in epidemiology and related disciplines, from coal through other occupations to the outdoor environment. The other is how, by doing so, it has contributed to a better understanding of a wide range of workplace and environmental risks and diseases, and how they might be prevented.

Coal research

In chapter 1 the two fundamental questions the PFR was designed to answer were noted:

- How much and what kinds of dust cause pneumoconiosis?
- What environmental conditions should be maintained if mineworkers are not to be disabled by the dust they breathe during the course of their work?[1]

These simple questions conceal the difficulties of what must in the 1950s have seemed a study of almost unimaginable scale and complexity, requiring a major organisational effort and the use of methods that were not yet available. But, in very simple terms, it was necessary not only to find a relationship between amount of dust inhaled and risk of pneumoconiosis, but also to discover what in the dust caused the disease, and what if any relationships existed between dust exposure, pneumoconiosis, other lung disease and disablement. The epidemiological part of this detective work, based on collecting and analysing data from coal miners during their lives, is described here. The pathological part, based on studies of miners' lungs following autopsy, is in chapter 7. The two approaches complemented each other in coming to the final conclusions.

Before considering the methods and results, it is helpful to understand two issues. First, coal mine dust varies in its constituents between collieries and time periods. It had long been disputed whether pneumoconiosis was caused by carbon, the main energy-producing constituent of coal itself, or by other components such as quartz or silicates. Resolving this was important for effective control. Secondly, the range and severity of effect on the lungs was also disputed: did it cause only pneumoconiosis or did it also cause chronic bronchitis and emphysema, later called chronic obstructive pulmonary disease (COPD)? This was important for understanding the level of disablement. Therefore, the key variables to investigate were exposure to airborne coal mine dust and its constituents as risk factors, with smoking as a confounder,[2] and measurements of effects on radiographs, symptoms and lung function as potential responses to the exposures. It was the good fortune of IOM that it was founded at a time when the PFR was ripe for such analysis.

Studying the miners

As outlined in chapter 1, the Pneumoconiosis Field Research (PFR) was started in 1953 by the then newly nationalised National Coal Board (NCB). Its design involved medical surveys at approximately five-year intervals of coal miners employed at the time of survey in collieries chosen to reflect the diversity of conditions in the UK coalfields.[1] The first series of surveys (PFR1), at twenty-five collieries, included chest radiographs ('x-rays'); later surveys (PFR2 and PFR3 at twenty-four of these pits, PFR4 and PFR5 at ten of these until 1977, and PFR6 at two of the ten) included in addition lung function, height, weight, and questionnaires of respiratory symptoms and smoking history.[3,4] [figs 5.1 and 5.2] A history of the individual miners' work in the coal industry up to that time was taken at the first PFR survey that he attended. In all, more than 50,000 miners were surveyed at least once,[3] with more than 30,000 at PFR1 alone.[4]

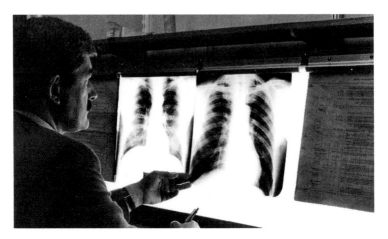

Fig 5.1: Reading x-rays as part of the PFR programme (c.1979)

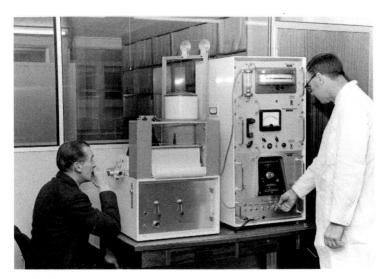

Fig 5.2: Spirometry testing of lung function, in the physiology lab at IOM (c.1975)

Exposure assessment

The estimation of these miners' exposures to airborne coal mine dust and its constituents was extraordinary both in the novelty of its design and in the comprehensiveness of dust assessment. Work at each colliery was divided into a set of occupational groups (OGs), typically 6-10 in any coal seam; OGs were revised as needed as the mining work progressed.[5] Researchers located at the collieries recorded, for every miner, the shifts he worked in each OG. They also managed and carried out a detailed programme of sampling full-shift dust concentrations in these OGs, with groundbreaking use of statistical methods to optimise sampling efficiency.[6] Long after its development, the PFR dust measurement methodology continued to win high praise from international experts, in the USA and the Netherlands.[7,8]

A suitable dust measurement instrument was of course also essential; the fundamental breakthrough in this had been the development (described in chapter 6) of what became known as the MRE113A sampler.[9] This gave the mass per unit volume of air (in units of mg/m^3) where the sampler was located, close to miners in the selected OG, typically for a full working shift including travel time. When gravimetric sampling was introduced as standard in the PFR, an extensive exercise was carried out to develop 'conversion factors', specific to coal seams underground, so that the earlier particle count data could be converted to gravimetric units.[10]

Laboratory analysis of samples combined across groups of OGs gave the percentages of coal, silica, kaolin, mica and other constituents of the airborne dust of the combined group.[11] Relevant data were then combined to give estimates of individuals' exposures to mixed coal mine dust and its constituents for particular time periods, notably the inter-survey periods (ISPs) between surveys at that colliery. Individuals' dust exposures prior to the initial survey attended were also estimated; unavoidably, these had greater uncertainties.

Using chest radiographs to classify pneumoconiosis

Other than *post-mortem*, coal workers' pneumoconiosis (CWP) is categorised by a reader (not necessarily a radiologist or even a doctor) recording small opacities on chest radiographs as CWP categories 0, 1, 2 or 3 according to their profusion. In one of the early PFR's many major methodological developments, this classification system devised by the Medical Research Council (MRC) in Cardiff was later extended to a twelve-point scale by asking whether, before one of the main categories was chosen, another (adjacent) one was seriously considered.[12] Large opacities, signifying the more serious condition of progressive massive fibrosis (PMF), are also recorded [figs 5.3a and 5.3b]. Radiological classification is necessarily

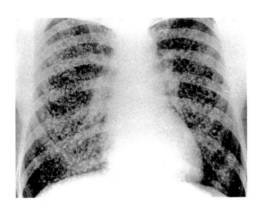

Fig 5.3(a): Chest radiograph of a coal miner with high silica exposure, showing category 3 simple pneumoconiosis

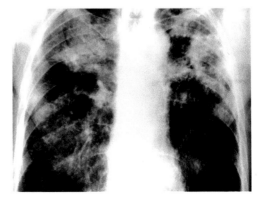

Fig 5.3(b): Chest radiograph of coal miner with progressive massive fibrosis in the upper part of both lungs

subjective but, with appropriate training of x-ray readers, acceptable reproducibility can be obtained,[13] and for many years now the system has been maintained and developed by the International Labour Organization (ILO). Dr Michael Jacobsen, IOM's Head of Statistics, pursued a long-term interest in this methodology while at IOM, and indeed subsequently in USA and Germany;[14] for example, the IOM trained a panel which, under Jacobsen's supervision, used the ILO classification in many other studies, including for asbestos-related x-ray appearances.

Coal mine dust and pneumoconiosis

Earliest key results, in 1969-71, were based on analysing the risks of developing simple pneumoconiosis over an approximately ten-year period (between PFR1 and PFR3) in a group of 4122 miners, mostly coalface workers, from twenty of the twenty-four research collieries.[15] The key paper, with Jacobsen as main author, was published in *Nature* in 1970;[16] further details were presented at the Inhaled Particles Conference in London in 1970 and published in 1971 in the two-volume Conference Proceedings, Inhaled Particles III.[17]

Radiographs had been classified by five trained and experienced physicians. Among miners without pneumoconiosis at initial survey, analyses of each film reader's results showed that the risk of Category 2 or more CWP at later survey increased clearly with higher airborne mixed dust exposures in the inter-survey period (and not, for example, with quartz concentrations). This was crucial in clarifying what aspect of the dust underground most needed to be regulated and reduced [fig 5.4].

Using a novel application of statistical Markov chain analysis,[18] the resulting dust-related risks of developing simple pneumoconiosis over a ten-year period were adapted to provide corresponding quantitative estimates of developing CWP (Cat 2 or more) over a thirty-five-year working lifetime. These derived dust-related lifetime risks then became the scientific basis for dust standards in UK coal mines and later in the USA.

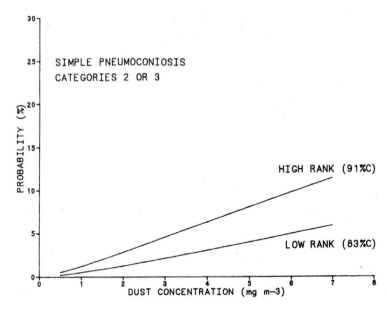

Fig 5.4: Risk of simple CWP categories 2 and 3 in relation to average dust exposure over a working lifetime. Risks increase with increasing coal rank (see page 173). Data based on 1987 analysis.

Later analyses in 1979-81, by Fintan Hurley and colleagues including Jacobsen, were based on miners who attended PFR3 and 5, many of whom had attended PFR1 also (i.e. had been in the PFR for twenty years). Hurley, a mathematician, had joined IOM as a statistician in 1975 "to do something useful". In a long career at IOM, including as Board member 1990-2017 and Scientific Director 2005-17, he was influential in helping maintain IOM's ethos and values in and through numerous organisational changes. The 1979-81 PFR analyses confirmed that mixed airborne coal mine dust exposure was the best predictor of CWP risk. Also, the dust-related lifetime risks of developing CWP (Cat 2 or more), now estimated directly, were similar to those made ten years earlier.[19] Further research led by Dr Colin Soutar, involving new surveys of ex-miners, showed very similar exposure-response relationships, implying that standards based on results for working miners were indeed protective of men generally.[20] Later, in a relatively small study of 895 coal miners, Heather Collins and co-workers found that small irregular opacities, though affecting fewer coalminers than the rounded opacities on which CWP was based, were also dust-related; and miners with small irregular opacities also had lower lung function than would be expected based on age, physique, smoking habit and dust exposure.[21]

Dust standards were based on controlling the occurrence of simple pneumoconiosis, not because of the limitations it caused (a miner might well be unaware of having it), but because it was a step, then understood as a necessary one, on the way to developing progressive massive fibrosis (PMF), a disabling and life-shortening condition. PFR results in the mid-1980s examined PMF and dust exposures directly; they showed clear relationships between cumulative mixed dust exposures and development of PMF over ten-year periods[3] and confirmed once again the core relationships with CWP that underpinned the dust standards.[22] Further analyses showed little evidence of deterioration of simple CWP, but there was a small risk of progression to develop the more serious PMF after ceasing work, the risk rising with increasing category of simple disease.[23]

The extensive and detailed research effort of the PFR, with its numerous methodological developments, had finally uncovered much of the story of coal mine dust and simple pneumoconiosis, and provided (and reconfirmed) the scientific basis for dust standards in British coal mines. There remained one puzzle: was there really no role for quartz exposure?

Quartz and silicosis

It had been argued since the 1930s that lung disease in coal miners was primarily caused by quartz in the inhaled dust, and that carbon itself was harmless; this belief still had adherents into the 1980s, despite PFR showing that generally the risks related not to quartz but to the amount of mixed coal mine dust inhaled. However, in the late 1970s, at an old PFR colliery south of Edinburgh where pneumoconiosis had previously been uncommon, a number of miners were found to have developed an unusually rapid progression of radiological change, including PMF; they had been exposed to airborne mixed dust with a high proportion of quartz from cutting stone in the roof and floor when coal seams narrowed.[24] Toxicological studies confirmed the greater virulence of such freshly cut quartz compared with that of 'old' quartz, embedded long term within the coal seam itself. They also demonstrated that in mixed dust the effect of quartz may be reduced by other silicate minerals such as kaolinite in the dust cloud. Analyses of data from a wider set of PFR collieries confirmed similar rapid progression of simple pneumoconiosis (CWP) in the presence of airborne coal mine dust of unusually high quartz content, i.e. above about 10% of the mixed dust.[19,25]

A subsequent follow-up of miners and ex-miners who had worked in the original colliery in the 1970s confirmed that category of pneumoconiosis was strongly related to exposures experienced in the 1970s, especially quartz;[26] and that the risks were much higher when that quartz exposure was experienced as high concentrations over a short timeframe.[27] The mine itself closed but the data on the effects of quartz figured prominently when Soutar and IOM colleagues summarised the key results from the PFR relevant to the setting of occupational standards.[28]

Measuring respiratory symptoms and lung function

At each PFR survey except PFR1, a questionnaire was administered of respiratory symptoms and smoking history, similar though not identical to that developed by the MRC in Cardiff. Also, measurements of spirometry (three single forced expirations, giving Forced Expired Volume in one second [FEV_1], Forced Vital Capacity [FVC], and the ratio of the two), were obtained from the miners who attended. Since the PFR objectives were to measure disability as well as pneumoconiosis, this was essential information; at the outset it was not known either whether pneumoconiosis in its early stages caused disablement, or whether any symptoms recorded were caused by smoking, which was known to be a common cause in the general population.

Dust exposure, respiratory symptoms and lung function

Analyses in the early 1970s of PFR3 data on lung function and on symptoms of chronic bronchitis (chronic cough and sputum) showed an expected clear adverse effect of smoking: current smokers had lower lung function and higher prevalence of chronic bronchitis than lifelong non-smokers.[29,30] After adjustment for smoking, there was also a clear relationship between higher dust exposure and lower lung function. Interestingly and importantly, this relationship was very similar in smokers and non-smokers; the two exposures seemed to be acting independently of one another.[29] Also, after adjustment for dust exposure as well as for smoking, lung function was unrelated to presence or severity of CWP.[31] PMF, the more severe radiologically-identified lung disease of coal miners, does lead to reduced lung function. Very similar results were found for symptoms of chronic bronchitis in younger miners – a clear relationship with dust exposure, no evidence that the relationship with dust exposure was different in smokers and non-smokers (although smokers had higher prevalence of chronic bronchitis) and no evidence that bronchitis and CWP were related, once dust exposure had been taken into account.[30] Corresponding relationships in older miners were not clear.

The key findings, that impairment of lung function and prevalence of chronic bronchitis were related to mixed coal mine dust exposure (and not to quartz in particular), were strengthened when Drs Richard Love and Brian Miller found that the degree of lung function loss over about ten years was related to miners' estimated dust exposures up to the start of the period; a relationship with concurrent dust exposure, i.e. during the ten-year period, was suggested but could have reflected other colliery-related differences.[32] Miller was a very able statistician who, over a thirty-five-year career at IOM, contributed widely to IOM's research on coal miners' lung disease (where he gained his PhD on dust-related causes of coal miners' mortality), other occupational epidemiology, and designed experimental work, especially mechanisms of disease. He is also a well-known and highly regarded traditional Scots singer, guitarist and teacher.

Further corroboration was found by Soutar and Hurley in later studies of miners and ex-miners, with similar results to those found in the 1970s.[33] Later analyses, by Hilary Cowie, Miller and Soutar, of data from nearly 7,000 miners examined the relationship between dust exposure, lung function and breathlessness, and gave new and better estimates of the effect of dust exposure on lung function.[34] Cowie is a versatile statistician who, in a long (and continuing) IOM career, led research projects in most of the areas of work, occupational and environmental, described in this chapter; and has contributed strongly to IOM's research management, including as IOM's Director of Research Operations. Separate analyses showed no clear relationships between estimated exposure to nitric oxide

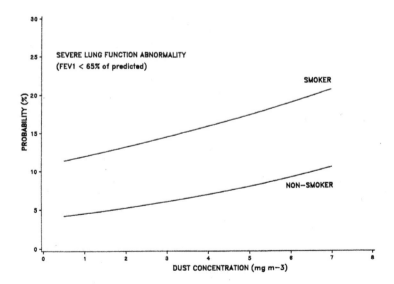

Fig 5.5: Risk of significant impairment of lung function in relation to average dust exposure in a working lifetime in smoking and non-smoking miners

(NO) and nitrogen dioxide (NO$_2$) (from use of diesels underground) and either respiratory infections or lung function.[35,36]

The emerging picture of miners' dust-related lung disability was clarified further by two studies in the later 1980s. Soutar and Hurley, in their study of miners and ex-miners, showed that dust exposure could cause clinically significant reductions of lung function.[37] In parallel work on a different PFR dataset, Dr Bill Marine, a visiting physician and epidemiologist from the USA, with IOM colleagues also focused on miners with clinically significant loss (to 65% of predicted value or less) [fig 5.5]. This easily-understood representation of lung function showed similar results: the risks were related to mixed dust exposure, not to quartz in particular; smoking was a major determinant and dust exposure was an additional burden – there was again no evidence of interaction or potentiation.[38,39]

Dust, quartz and coal miners' mortality

To assess what results such as these imply for coal miners' survival, Jacobsen secured help from the national death registration agencies in England, Wales and Scotland and, with Miller, studied dust exposure, pneumoconiosis, survival and mortality in a very large PFR dataset: 25,000 miners from twenty collieries followed up for about twenty-two years.[40] Like many groups of workers, coal miners' survival was better than that of the general population.[41] Overall, risks of mortality increased with estimated dust exposure, principally because of deaths from pneumoconiosis and COPD. Mortality risks did not vary with presence or severity of simple pneumoconiosis, but miners with PMF had clearly higher risk of death. Lung cancer mortality was clearly higher in smokers but not related to dust exposure. Interestingly, there was strongly suggestive evidence that higher dust exposure was related to digestive cancer, principally stomach cancer,[40] a finding also in Jacobsen's earlier work and in some studies elsewhere. More recent analyses, again based on a large sample of PFR miners (almost 18,000 men from ten collieries) but with better estimates of dust exposures, generally confirmed these earlier findings. However, the new analyses showed a relationship between lung cancer and cumulative exposure to quartz, especially when analyses included a fifteen-year time-lag between exposure and risk of death.[42]

Overview of PFR results: controversy and compensation

The PFR was undoubtedly world-leading research and produced clear associations between coal dust and quartz exposure and pneumoconiosis, and these have been used throughout the world to justify preventive standard-setting in industry. Coal dust exposure not only causes CWP but also is associated in a dose-response relationship with respiratory symptoms, loss of lung function and premature mortality. But these latter associations are not clearly related to the presence of CWP save when PMF occurs. Therein lies the controversy. The PFR results indicated that there are two separate consequences of coal dust exposure: CWP and COPD, the latter alone also being influenced by smoking. This result was challenged by others who believed that smoking alone caused COPD in miners and non-miners alike. The PFR evidence was ultimately accepted by the UK Industrial Injuries Advisory Council and COPD was accepted as an occupational disease of coal-miners. This led to compensation on a no-fault basis becoming available to miners with COPD who had worked for a qualifying period underground.

However, the mining unions took this further in Civil Law, proposing that the coal industry had been negligent in allowing miners to work in conditions likely to cause COPD and bringing forward several individual claimants. British Coal chose to defend this action, claiming that there was not reliable knowledge of the risks – an unexpected strategy of seeking to discredit the PFR and its findings, in spite of having funded all the research that led to understanding the relationship and being aware of this from regular reports from IOM. A very expensive and prolonged court case resulted which in effect challenged the science of the PFR and IOM. Jacobsen, who had led the analyses of exposure-response relationships from the beginnings of IOM in 1969, gave evidence and the British Coal attack on the PFR was wholly discredited, the miners receiving substantial damages. Some of the challenge to the PFR focused on the lung function findings of Marine, Derek Gurr and Jacobsen.[38] That controversy was revisited and summarised by Jacobsen's son Jonny, shortly after his father's death.[43] The UK Government then devised a system of paying general compensation to any coal miner who had COPD, a sum usually considerably greater than would be available from industrial injuries compensation.

Other industries

When IOM was set up as a charity in 1969, it was intended that its work should cover exposures and associated risks to health across industry generally, and not just in the coal industry. It was not long before IOM's skills, expertise and research culture in leading-edge exposure assessment were used in other industries also. The focus was on substantive results, to inform policy development, rather than on methodological novelty, although there have been important methodological developments also, as IOM expanded its capability to meet new challenges.

Coke and steel industries

The earliest other studies involved mortality of coke and steel workers. When coal is carbonised at very high temperatures in coke ovens for use as coke in steel-making and other industries, workers may be exposed to fumes containing benzene soluble materials (BSMs), some of which are carcinogens known as polycyclic aromatic hydrocarbons. In the early 1970s IOM was asked by the nationalised UK coal and steel industries to set up and carry out a mortality study of workers at their twenty-seven coke plants (plus a specialist Phurnacite plant and two tar works), studies in the USA having shown an increased risk of lung cancer, especially in workers at or near the ovens. Work histories were obtained from personnel records and summarised as individuals' years of working in various parts of the coke plant, especially on or near the ovens, and later linked with results from BSM sampling carried out by the companies in and around most of the coke ovens, to give improved estimates of men's exposure – a major exercise in working with industry staff to gather, verify, supplement and classify 'routine' data for research purposes.

In a series of reports and papers, from the late 1970s and intermittently through to 2013, the estimates of time worked and exposure to BSMs were linked with records of men's mortality obtained for research purposes from the national agencies in England and Wales, and in Scotland. Early results confirmed an excess of lung cancer among the nearly 7,000 coke workers studied, although the excess was not as severe as had been found in the USA and there was not a clear relationship with time worked on oven jobs.[44] The industry took protective measures, with better control of emissions and workers' use of respirators. While intermediate analyses suggested some relationships of lung cancer with estimated BSM exposures,[45] the most recent results remained inconclusive, with little evidence of an exposure-response relationship,[46] a puzzling finding in light of results elsewhere.

Later in the 1970s, the British Steel Corporation (BSC) asked IOM to take over a much bigger study of the mortality of steel workers generally, which the industry had undertaken and was proving difficult to do. This involved linking work histories, from personnel and pensions records, with mortality records for more than 85,000 industrial workers from forty-three BSC establishments of varying size across England, Scotland and Wales; the study had been collapsing in the face of the huge volume of work involved. Further work at IOM failed to overcome the flaws in cohort identification and completeness, and in quality of work histories; and despite strong efforts to salvage the study, results were limited[47] – a useful reminder that volume of data does not compensate for limitations of quality, although later analyses of a subset of 17,000 workers who had been employed for ten years or more suggested some areas of work-related excess mortality.[48]

Later, in the early 1990s, British Steel, responding to concerns about respiratory ill health in its workers in steel mills, commissioned a study in current workers of respiratory symptoms and cardiac risk factors in relation to occupations graded by dust exposure. This again involved a major exercise of working with industry staff, this time in the various medical departments of five integrated steel works, to gather research-quality cardio-respiratory medical measurements, together with work history, smoking history and other questionnaire data. Detailed statistical analysis found, perhaps surprisingly, no clear evidence of work-related respiratory or cardiovascular ill health.[49]

Polyvinyl chloride manufacture

The coke and steel mortality studies of the 1970s had involved gathering and linking existing personnel and mortality data about workers in specific industries; they did not involve actual new medical surveys of workers, for research purposes. The full IOM integrated research team for epidemiology[50] was in 1981 engaged for the first time in work outside of the coal industry. The chief medical officer of the major chemical company, ICI, approached IOM's Director, Dr Anthony Seaton, for an expert medical opinion on whether chest radiographs of particular workers who had been exposed occupationally to PVC dust showed signs of pneumoconiosis. This was at a time when liver cancer had been described in workers exposed to the gas from which PVC was made, vinyl chloride, and people in the industry were concerned that analogous effects might arise from PVC. Since there was no knowledge at the time of any effects of PVC, Seaton explained that a reading of radiographs would be insufficient to allay fears and proposed a new study to quantify any risks and determine what, if any, protection was needed for workers. The proposal was developed by Jacobsen and accepted and funded by ICI on what had become standard IOM terms – that while collaboration with the industry was essential to the conduct of the study,[51] the design, conduct and analysis of the study would be IOM's responsibility, the conclusions would be IOM's independent view of the evidence in the light of the work and the other evidence worldwide, and the methods and results of the whole study would be reported to the workforce and published openly.

The ICI study, led by Soutar assisted by a young chest physician, Dr Peter Thornley, was important in understanding the relationships between exposure to PVC dust and lung disease: it showed relationships between cumulative exposure and a range of respiratory outcomes (slight pneumoconiotic change on radiographs, mild chest symptoms and limited loss of lung function).[52] The effects were mild; without good study design and exposure assessment it might not have been possible to identify them. But on another level, the ICI study showed that IOM was able to negotiate and carry out a complex study for private industry, to a high quality and under time pressure, while maintaining full control of study interpretation and results. The results were reported to the workforce and proved important for the protection of workers in the UK and elsewhere, being used by the UK Health and Safety Executive (HSE) to define an exposure standard for PVC factories. A later IOM study of mortality of these workers showed findings that the authors considered reassuring: relatively low death rates from non-malignant lung disease and no direct evidence of a relationship with estimated PVC dust exposure; no good evidence of an effect on lung cancer; but some ambiguous results on ischaemic heart disease that support a prudent policy of keeping dust levels as low as practicable.[53]

The shale oil industry

Even more complex studies were to follow. In 1973 there was an international oil crisis and the USA began to exploit the reserves of oil contained underground in Rocky Mountain shale. This involved the mining of oil-containing shale and then crushing and heating the stone above ground to produce oil which was then refined to produce paraffin and petroleum products. This had been a pioneering industry in West Lothian near Edinburgh from about 1850 until the 1960s, and exposure to the raw paraffin product was one of the earliest described causes of occupational skin cancer. Coincidentally, Seaton in his clinical work discovered that shale miners had sometimes developed pneumoconiosis, though this had never previously been recognised. With IOM colleagues he analysed a surgically excised lung from one of his patients, discovered some other cases in the archives of a local hospital and wrote a paper pointing to a need to investigate possible hazards in the new USA workforce.[54] With help from colleagues in the US National Institute for Occupational Safety and Health, he obtained a grant from the US Department of Energy who were looking for information on which to base a risk assessment in the industry. He approached the Chief Medical Officer of BP, the company which had inherited the shale industry during its decline, for agreement to carry out a study, and found that by good fortune BP had retained pension records of employment of workers in the West Lothian shale industry during the 1940-60s. They agreed to IOM using them for research purposes. From this came three studies: a mortality study led by Miller of all those whose records had been found; a cross-sectional field study led by a research fellow seconded from South Africa, Dr Steve Louw, of those who had survived until the mid-1980s; and a community oral history study of conditions for workers and for the wider community in West Lothian, led by another research fellow, Dr Sarah Randall. All three were completed successfully [fig 5.6].

Fig 5.6: IOM mobile laboratory amongst the shale bings of West Lothian (c.1970)

The mortality study, which was supplemented with a case-control study of lung cancer in the local area in collaboration with a chest physician, Dr Wilson Middleton, was reassuring in that it showed no excess risk of lung cancer in shale workers (including refinery employees). It did, however, confirm the risk of skin cancer in these workers.[55] The study of surviving workers showed a low risk of pneumoconiosis, although it was impossible to make estimates of dust exposure. In these circumstances it was argued that for any new US industry a dust standard similar to that for coal would be appropriate.[56] The community study used qualitative methods and gave interesting insight into the social conditions of shale workers in the first half of the 20th century, an early venture by IOM into this sort of qualitative social research that was not pursued later.[57]

Wool workers

An asthmatic type of lung disease called byssinosis had long been recognised in cotton workers in Lancashire. In the early 1980s trade unions representing workers in the Yorkshire wool textile industry suspected that these employees might be suffering similar respiratory problems though curiously this had never been studied. It was known to some physicians that occasionally individuals became allergic to wool, but no specific disease of wool workers had been described. The trade union obtained agreement from HSE that it would fund a study and approached IOM through Seaton.

The industry was complex, being separated into multiple specialised factories carrying out the different processes required to transform raw wool from sheep and goats into fine quality woven material, but all had a common characteristic of exposing workers to wool dust, generally a rather coarse fibrous material, very different from coal. It was apparent that exposure required to be measured differently to represent this type of dust. Fortunately, Dr Jim Vincent and his colleagues in the physics branch had recently patented a suitable inhalable dust sampler; this study provided an opportunity to validate this in a real-life situation and incidentally led to it being recognised as the standard instrument for such investigations, now known as the IOM inhalable dust sampler.[58]

Study of the workers was complicated not only by the many different workplaces but also by the fact that a third of them spoke Urdu with little command of English, so the questionnaire was translated and then retranslated to ensure that it captured the symptoms of interest. The study was designed by Seaton, Jacobsen and Jim Dodgson and the field work was successfully led by Love. The analyses showed that workers were indeed at risk of respiratory symptoms in relation to the amount of wool dust they were being exposed to.[59] However, no radiological abnormalities were found, and this seemed to be primarily an airway disease caused by inhaling irritant wool fibres.[60] This unique study was used by HSE to set a dust standard for wool factories.

Quarries and brickworks

During the 1980s Soutar, as the new head of the medical branch, negotiated and led several cross-sectional field studies on lung disease and exposure to quartz and silicates, in industries such as Scottish quarries and the heavy clay or brickworks industry. Together with work on silica in coal mining, this gave IOM a strong base in the epidemiology of non-biological workplace dusts.

Study design and conduct followed by now familiar lines as a team effort between medical, occupational hygiene, statistical and data management colleagues, but each study had its nuances. In the brickworks, for example, some plants had old traditional Hoffman kilns and some had modern tunnel ones. Statistical analysis of dust sampling showed higher dust concentrations at or near the traditional kilns than the modern ones. In a nice example of interdisciplinary collaboration, the IOM project team showed that the 'obvious' explanation, that this was a consequence of modern engineering and kiln design, was wrong. Graeme Wetherill, the project statistician, conjectured that if this were the cause, there would not be a corresponding difference in concentrations upstream of the kilns, near the start of the production process. But there was; and further investigation by Sheila Groat, the lead occupational hygienist, found that typically, when a new tunnel kiln had been introduced, 'housekeeping' had been improved right throughout the process;[61] it was this general improvement, rather than only the kiln type, which caused the reduction in dust concentrations. The prevalence of respiratory disease was low, but with some evidence that pneumoconiosis was related to quartz exposures while chronic bronchitis and breathlessness were associated with dust exposures.[61]

The study of Scottish quarry workers, funded by HSE and led by Dr Raymond Agius, was interesting methodologically in that a large amount of dust and quartz concentration data were available from routine sampling across the industry (over 1,700 samples from 300 surveys at eighty-six quarries). To check the reliability of these data for research purposes, IOM carried out an intensive monitoring exercise of three one-week-long surveys, one each in winter, summer and spring or autumn, at each of four quarries. The results of this special exercise showed that dust and quartz concentrations varied with production levels, weather, work practices and dust control. These factors largely explained differences between the research and compliance sampling results[62] and enabled the compliance data from other quarries to be used for exposure estimation. Results showed a clear association between estimated cumulative exposure to respirable dust and profusion of small rounded opacities, some of which may represent silicosis. The authors recommended that dust be controlled especially in the dustiest occupations and quarries.[63]

Opencast coal mining

Not uncommonly, industrial activities give rise to health concerns among local communities from exposure to pollution, and such concerns can be addressed by specific epidemiological studies, for which IOM was and is well qualified and its independence respected. For example, an opencast coal mine was subject to complaints of asthma in the adjacent community, and the industry body, Opencast, commissioned an epidemiological study of workers within several opencast sites. The frequency of asthmatic and other symptoms in the workers was not related to exposure to dust in the industry, suggesting that the process was unlikely to be a cause of asthma.[64]

Mineral fibres

Non-biological workplace dusts of course include fibres and, notoriously, asbestos. Could an active research base in fibre measurement (chapter 6) and toxicology (chapter 7) be supplemented by epidemiology? With respect to asbestos, there was a clear need. At IOM, and with industry support and co-operation, Jacobsen led a detailed pilot study showing that epidemiology was feasible also, but the industry did not fund it.

Through the 1970s and 80s, IOM did, however, participate in several major studies of synthetic mineral fibres, through development and implementation of exposure assessment methods, led by Dodgson and Cherrie. IOM's work on exposure assessment was linked to and part of a series of international epidemiology studies led by IARC, the International Agency for Research on Cancer in Lyon, France; both the exposure assessment and the epidemiology are described in chapter 6.

Later, in the 1990s, IOM led international collaborative studies of the respiratory health, and of the mortality, of refractory ceramic fibre (RCF) workers in England, France and Germany. A three-way research collaboration was set up with two other well-established epidemiology units, INRS in France and the University of Cologne (to which Jacobsen had moved after leaving IOM) in Germany. The studies were straightforward in principle, being similar in concept and in design to many field studies and mortality studies that IOM had conducted successfully, with linked exposure assessment, field epidemiology of respiratory disease and a mortality study. In practice there were difficulties, however, partly because of the studies' international dimension: issues of language, obviously, and of laws and custom also – the laws concerning access to and linkage of data differed markedly in the three countries.

But bigger problems arose because of inadequate communication between the research team and occupational hygienists at the RCF companies' factories. The project's exposure assessment strategy, based as usual on occupational groups (OGs) of workers experiencing similar dust concentrations, required taking multiple samples in a standardised manner across different OGs on any given day of sampling, in order to help estimate average OG concentrations. This is quite different from the more forensic sampling carried out by experienced company hygienists, which typically focused on problem areas only, with limited numbers of samples per day, and detailed characterisation of the tasks being carried out by the workers wearing samplers, in order to identify and understand where the high concentrations were being experienced and what could be done about them. To the company hygienists, the research sampling seemed inefficient and of poor quality.[65] Clearly, better communication was needed of what the research sampling was trying to achieve overall, and of how the number and location of samples supported those aims. Once this had happened, and was set up in an ongoing way, all went well again.

In the event, all aspects of the research were completed successfully. Results did not suggest any serious problems: they showed little or no evidence of dust-related pneumoconiosis, some evidence of dust-related mild loss of lung function but in current workers only, and a possible association between recent dust exposures and chronic bronchitis, although overall symptom prevalence was low.[66]

Pesticides and other potentially toxic exposures

Diversification continued, with studies for HSE and other UK Government departments of the respiratory health of beef and dairy farmers (there were problems in studying a dispersed workforce) and of farmers and other workers involved in sheep dipping, and so exposed to organophosphate pesticides (OPs), to prevent infestations.[67] An exposure-response study was needed, but information on past and present exposures to OP pesticides was not available. An innovative sequence of studies was designed by Soutar and led by Dr Adele Pilkington, Christine Sewell and Duncan Buchanan. Pilkington was an occupational physician who, in a relatively short career at IOM, made a major contribution both to research and to the development of occupational health services. An initial study of urine metabolites of organophosphates in sheep dippers together with observation of the tasks they performed enabled the exposures typical of the tasks to be identified. Then a questionnaire asking about past and present participation in these tasks and a standard questionnaire designed to identify neurological symptoms were administered to a much larger population of sheep dippers and controls, together with some tests of peripheral nerve function. By combining the task histories with the task/exposure relations, an index of exposure could be calculated for each person. A weak relation between symptoms and exposure was demonstrated, and this was largely accounted for by a strong relation with tasks in which the concentrate was handled.[68] And the initial exposure assessment study revealed that highly undesirable practices were commonplace and potential exposures were often high. Official guidance on safe practice followed, changing the ways that pesticides were stored, sold and used. Other work on pesticides followed, especially concerning exposure during crop spraying, including bystander exposure.[69]

Responding to concerns that exposure of soldiers to aerosols of depleted uranium from missiles during the Iraq War had led to chronic uranium poisoning, the Ministry of Defence commissioned a study of uranium levels in the urine of returning soldiers. The study, in collaboration with the Institute of Naval Medicine for uranium analysis, demonstrated very low levels of urinary uranium.[70]

Other occupational cancers

Reports of cancer among workers at a semi-conductor facility in Greenock near Glasgow had caused concern to workers and the local community, partly because of similar reports at some other facilities internationally. Following its initial investigation, HSE then asked IOM to collaborate with it in a joint study of exposure and mortality. The study was characterised by a very detailed historical hygiene assessment led by Dr Karen Galea, now Head of Exposure Assessment at IOM, of working conditions throughout the semi-conductor plant.[71] Correspondingly detailed statistical analyses by Miller and others failed to find evidence of work-related cancer.[72]

Dr Damien McElvenny, at that time with HSE, but now principal epidemiologist at IOM, was a key researcher in the semi-conductor project. In the early 2000s, while still at HSE, he initiated a research project to understand the number of cases of cancer caused by work and to develop appropriate practical measures to reduce the incidence. The work was undertaken by scientists at Imperial College London (ICL), the Health and Safety Laboratory (HSL), Cranfield University and IOM, and led by Dr Lesley Rushton from ICL. The estimates relied on detailed information about the number of workers employed in different sectors, the carcinogenic hazards present in these jobs and the likely level of risk associated with the work. Cherrie and another experienced exposure scientist, Dr Martie van Tongeren, who later became IOM Research Director before moving to a professorship at the University of Manchester, were involved in providing advice on the exposure in different sectors and the way that exposures had changed over time.[73]

Preliminary results for six types of cancer were published in 2007 and the researchers then embarked on an ambitious plan to estimate the burden for all occupational cancers from all work, and to estimate how this might change in the future with additional regulatory or other interventions. The final results were published in the *British Journal of Cancer* in 2012.[74] Overall, around 8,000 cancer deaths and 14,000 cancer registrations were attributable to work; the deaths accounted for around one in twenty of all cancer deaths in Britain. The research highlighted the importance of a small number of types of cancer, including mesothelioma, lung, nasopharynx, breast, and non-melanoma skin cancer, and key causal carcinogens such as asbestos, mineral oils, solar radiation, silica, diesel engine exhaust and coal tars and pitches. It also highlighted that with strict interventions more than 80% of occupational cancers could be avoided.

Following on from this work Cherrie led further projects, to estimate the cancer risks for all workers in Europe for a range of carcinogens to assist the European Commission update legislation for occupational carcinogens,[75] and to estimate the cancer and non-malignant respiratory disease burden in the construction sector in Singapore. IOM's work for the European Commission has been used to underpin the final revisions of the Carcinogens and Mutagens Directive, which will influence the way all European organisations manage workplace carcinogens in the future.

These studies have helped focus attention on the importance of work-related cancers; in Britain 144 workers were killed in accidents in 2018, compared to around 8,000 estimated deaths from occupational cancer. The Institution of Occupational Safety and Health (IOSH), the premier international health and safety practitioner organisation, has subsequently developed its influential No Time to Lose campaign (www.NoTimeToLose.org. uk) to raise awareness of the occupational cancer problem and promote effective solutions to its members and others. Cherrie and Rushton have provided ongoing support for the campaign, including further specific research reviews and supporting materials. Independently, the British Occupational Hygiene Society (BOHS) produced a similar campaign on cancer and other risks in construction (http://www.breathefreely.org.uk). These campaigns, inspired in large part by the research that IOM has helped undertake, are having an important impact on reducing the future cancer risks of workers.

Human factors

Finally, a stream of research on human factors was established by and with IOM's Ergonomics branch, and this was integrated fully into IOM's wider research activities after Ergonomics transferred to the Edinburgh headquarters of IOM in 1990. The story of the Ergonomics branch is given in chapter 8. It included experimental research on lifting, on noise and on thermal stress, as well as survey-based research on the effectiveness of regulations. It also included epidemiology, which took similar methods of design and analysis as had underpinned the epidemiological research on dusts and chemicals and applied these methods into the different contexts of exposure assessment and medical measurement implied by human factors research. These were 'new' in the sense that the health outcomes were principally musculoskeletal (e.g. back pain, upper limb disease), and the risk factors of interest were physical activities such as lifting and repetitive keyboard work, or psychological such as degree of control over one's work environment, rather than dusts and chemicals.

Transfer of IOM's established expertise to these new contexts was both interesting and difficult: interesting in the challenge of using our experience to develop methods of exposure assessment and medical assessment in areas where such methods were not yet well established in the general literature; difficult in that funding for studies almost always underestimated the scale of method development required, and sought substantive results as if methods were already well established.

However, some significant methodological advances were made, notably a questionnaire developed by Agius and colleagues, for identifying back pain for use in epidemiological studies.[76] This was linked to several studies of back pain in coal miners carried out by IOM in the later 1980s and early 1990s. One such study included development by Dr Richard Graveling and human factors colleagues of a questionnaire for "lifting, carrying, holding, pushing, pulling and use of transport systems underground".[77] The associated case-control study, led by Dr Eugene Waclawski, of miners' sickness absence due to back pain, found a relationship only with frequency of lifting very heavy weights (lifting more than 50 kg with a frequency of more than twenty times in a shift).[77]

One study which illustrates the issues focused on the effects of lifting during pregnancy on birth outcomes. This included interesting prior discussion about possible mechanisms of effect, e.g. that occasional lifting of very heavy loads in later pregnancy might 'trigger' premature birth, whereas consistently lifting quite heavy loads throughout pregnancy might imply chronic tiredness and low birth weight for gestational age. The challenge was to design and carry out a study which allowed these various possible mechanisms to be investigated. Participants at an ante-natal clinic were asked to record the heaviest weight lifted in a day and the heaviest frequently lifted weight (where "frequently" was defined as five or more times in a day), on each day during the last trimester of pregnancy. Although "a considerable number of participants in this study lifted weights, some of them on a regular basis, which might be considered to present a degree of risk to healthy non-pregnant females", no relationship with birthweight was found.[78] Dr Kevin Tesh and co-authors concluded that, while firm generalisations could not be made, the study suggested that current regulations were sufficiently protective.

The largest and most complex of these studies concerned the effects of keyboard work on the risk and development of upper limb disorders (ULD). There was an initial study of keyboard workers, to develop a methodology of exposure assessment – what characteristics of the keyboard operators' work might be related to ULD and how could these be recorded systematically and in a standardised manner. Ideally the epidemiology would have been a prospective study, following forward in time the experience of a study cohort without ULD at the start of the study, classifying the exposure of individual workers, identifying the development of signs and symptoms of ULD, and examining how these related to exposure characteristics. This, however, would have taken too long and been too costly. Instead, a case-control study was carried out, whereby individuals with ULD ('cases') were compared with keyboard workers without the condition ('controls'). Being female, and older, increased the risk of being a case. There was, however, a difficulty: while the aim was to identify work patterns before onset of disease and compare those with controls, many workers with ULD had understandably adapted their working habits to compensate for the condition. Consequently, the exposure assessment included not only observation of current work practices but interview assessment of how these had changed in the light of signs and symptoms of ULD; and integration of these two aspects of exposure history. Results showed that risks increased with number of hours per week spent using a keyboard, with duration of keyboard working without a break, and with a number of psychosocial factors indicating stress – results which supported protective regulations introduced in the UK in 1992.[79]

Other science-policy occupational research

Other noteworthy IOM research, not otherwise easily classifiable, falls broadly in the area of science-policy links. For example, the records of the Pneumoconiosis Field Research proved a valuable resource for investigating on behalf of HSE the quantitative relationship between mineral dust exposure and lung functional deficits, work that was later extended to consider the applicability of these risk estimates to chemically inert insoluble dusts in general.[80] Also for HSE, Peter Ritchie led the development of a prototype Sickness Absence Recording Tool (SART), for recording, monitoring and analysing sickness absence as a means to better manage sickness absence and return to work; HSE made this available for free download from its website.[81] Additionally for HSE, IOM collaborated in an interesting assessment of the true costs of occupational asthma in the UK and found that while the costs to society are high, "the economic burden falls on the state and the individual, not on the employer. The incentive for employers to act is thus weak."[82]

Change of research commissioning strategy at HSE
IOM's need to diversify further

Through the 1990s and early 2000s IOM's research had diversified to the point where, by a clear margin, the UK Government's Health and Safety Executive (HSE) rather than the UK coal industry had become its single largest funder. This was mostly through research contracts won individually in open competition, which sometimes included against HSE's own research teams at its Health and Safety Laboratories (HSL). However, in 2006, shortly after HSL had moved to new premises, HSE took a strategic decision to have as much as possible of its research done in-house at HSL and limit correspondingly its programme of funded extra-mural research. This reduced markedly an important source of funding for occupational research at IOM and associated IOM links with the development of workplace policy. Occupational research continued at IOM, however, with some ongoing work for HSE (including some in collaboration with HSL) and with diverse sources of funding (see chapter 2).

The adverse impact on IOM was reduced because of the development, through the 1990s and beyond, of research on environmental exposures and health, especially outdoor air pollution, to which we now turn; and the later development of a major research theme on the risks and safety of engineered nanoparticles, for which see chapter 9.

Environment and public health

Costing the effects of pollution

IOM's science-policy work on the environment began in the early 1990s, as part of a major EU-funded set of projects on the external costs[83] of energy (ExternE).[84] ExternE was set up to answer the question, How would the actual and relative costs of producing electricity in various ways change, if the polluter had to pay for damages to the environment over the whole life cycle of production? This included how electricity generation (or later, how various modes of transport) caused emissions which dispersed, travelled (through air, soil and water) and changed over space and time, affecting the exposure of individuals and consequently their health. Major development of methods by a large EU-wide interdisciplinary team was needed to assess the impacts on human health, on ecology and on non-living materials, from production of raw materials (e.g. coal mining, building solar panels) through to waste disposal (e.g. nuclear and other); and then to provide credible monetary valuation of these multiple effects.

IOM, through Hurley, became involved in ExternE in 1992, initially to propose exposure-response functions for the health effects of coal mining, as part of assessing the impacts of generating electricity from coal. It soon became clear that within the 'coal fuel cycle' of electricity generation, by far the greatest damage to human health came from air pollution from coal-fuelled power stations; and IOM's role developed rapidly to include developing methods for quantifying the health impacts of outdoor air pollution, first from various modes of electricity generation, then from transport. This was at a time when it was becoming apparent that there was no 'safe' level of outdoor particulate matter (PM).[85] At that time, however, the evidence on air pollution and health was strongly contested – scientifically, it used advanced statistical methods and was counter-intuitive to many experts on disease mechanisms; and economically, the implications were potentially huge. A lot of money hinged on the validity of the evidence, and there were sustained attacks on the integrity of key air pollution epidemiologists in the USA, attacks which proved to be completely unfounded.

It was a big challenge to review the international evidence and propose risk functions for quantifying the health effects of outdoor air pollution EU-wide, in this controversial and high-profile area, new to IOM.[86] However, the ExternE methodology, first published in 1995, included an extensive description by IOM (Hurley and Dr Peter Donnan) of what became known as health impact assessment (HIA) of ambient air pollution.[87] This methodology proved robust and soon became influential and used (with local adaptation of some methods) in numerous projects across Europe, both at

EU level and within particular countries.[88] For example, in one local application by IOM, Dr Alison Searl refined the ExternE HIA methodology for application in Scotland, in a project commissioned by the Scottish Office to investigate the likely impact of air pollution on mortality in Central Scotland.[89] Searl was a geology PhD who had joined IOM in 1995 as Head of Laboratory Services. A very able scientist across many disciplines, she became an established researcher in exposure assessment, toxicology and health impact assessment, and a leading international consultant on the health effects of environmental pollutants. She used similar methods in a HIA of the proposed Low Emission Zone in London.

The ExternE methodology for HIA was developed further by Hurley and IOM colleagues (Miller, Cowie, Donnan, Searl, Pilkington and others) within a series of other projects, mostly funded from the Fifth and Sixth Framework Programmes of the European Commission.[90] This included as far as possible using European risk functions and developing substantially the methods for mortality assessment. This led to the most high-profile application, during development of the European Commission's flagship Clean Air for Europe (CAFE) programme in 2005/06, when an IOM update of the ExternE HIA methodology became a core and integral part of the Commission's health impact assessment and cost-benefit analysis of the entire CAFE programme.[91] The results showed that the expected benefits to human health of technically feasible reductions in air pollution across the EU far exceeded the costs of these reductions, and so provided an economic justification, based on health benefits, of the Commission's measures to improve air quality EU-wide.

Understanding deaths from pollution

A key part of IOM's success in HIA of outdoor air pollution was work developed principally by Miller on quantifying the effects on mortality of long-term exposure to air pollution. In 1993 and 1995 results from two major cohort studies in the USA indicated that long-term exposure to outdoor air pollution, that is through living long term in more heavily polluted cities, increased the age-specific risks of death; and suggested that this longer-term exposure had a far greater impact on public health than the more-or-less immediate initiation of effects caused by higher daily pollution which until then had been driving both quantified assessment and air quality policy. Again, these results were contested; and while the UK Department of Health (DoH) Committee on the Medical Effects of Air Pollutants (COMEAP) initially remained agnostic,[85] they were incorporated in a preliminary way into the ExternE methodology on a 'what if' basis as early as 1995.[87]

International consensus on the importance of long-term exposure grew, and led to a major methodological challenge: how to express meaningfully for science-policy purposes the popular notion of *excess* deaths due to pollution when everybody dies eventually? Clearly the issue is how to quantify the effect of pollution on *age at death* rather than the fact of death itself, an issue resolved by Miller in the later 1990s, and refined subsequently by him and others.

Miller worked out a detailed methodology for applying statistical life table methods to calculate, using the results of the cohort studies, how air pollution affects mortality in real populations. This includes effects both on life expectancy and on the population's total survival time, i.e. aggregated years lived by the population as a whole. This gave practical implementation to some earlier ideas by Professor Bert Brunekreef in the Netherlands and parallel but highly theoretical work in ExternE by Dr Ari Rabl in France. The associated main published paper[92] and IOMLIFET,[93] the set of linked Excel spreadsheets and associated instructions for implementation developed by Miller, became a kind of industry standard for use of life tables in estimating the effects of outdoor air pollution on mortality, including influencing the World Health Organization's AirQ computing program for health impact assessment of outdoor air pollution. Miller's life tables work was supported strongly and actively by Dr Bob Maynard, senior medical officer for air quality at the UK Department of Health (DoH) in London, and his colleague Dr Heather Walton, including with DoH funding.

Science-policy links

Research in the UK on air pollution and health had been reinvigorated through the early 1990s, with Maynard playing a key role in arranging funding for and overviewing a multi-layered research programme, overseen by COMEAP, of which Seaton was a member. Although IOM's quantification work on ExternE was initially outside the mainstream of this effort, at Seaton's suggestion Maynard invited Hurley, then lead scientist on risk quantification for human health in ExternE, to be part of a 1993-95 COMEAP working group on assessing the health effects of non-biological ambient particles. This led to a long association of IOM with COMEAP: at one point all three of Hurley, Miller and Searl were members. Sometimes seemingly small contributions can be influential: Hurley's proposed change of the major conclusion of COMEAP's 1995 report on particles and health from "it would be prudent to consider the associations as causal" to "it would be imprudent not to consider the associations as causal" was accepted. While the formulation was awkward, the meaning was clear – in a controversial area, COMEAP had clearly come to the view that ambient particles were indeed doing serious damage to human health.[85] This clarity significantly strengthened the hand of those, in the UK and elsewhere, seeking to introduce better controls on ambient particles.

Much more substantially, Miller and Hurley made central contributions to COMEAP's highly regarded and highly influential 2010 report on ambient particles and mortality,[94] which was based largely on Miller's life tables work; and more recently Hurley played a major role in developing what became COMEAP's majority view on quantifying jointly the mortality impacts of particulate matter and nitrogen dioxide (NO_2).[95] Either or both also participated in various international science-policy working groups on air quality and health, particularly of the World Health Organization,[96] of the EU and of the US EPA, as part of international efforts to understand the effect of air pollution on human health and in particular assess the likely benefits of measures to reduce ambient pollution.

Air pollution epidemiology – international studies

Perhaps curiously, IOM had little active involvement in primary epidemiology on outdoor air pollution. Through the 1990s and subsequently, former IOM lead scientists were now also active in the field, with Seaton at Aberdeen and Professor Ken Donaldson in Edinburgh making major contributions to an understanding of disease mechanisms (see chapter 7). Seaton was active more widely, including as Chair of the UK Expert Panel on Air Quality Standards (EPAQS); he involved Miller as statistician on some epidemiological studies led from Aberdeen. Local air pollution research in Edinburgh and Central Scotland was led by Agius, another former IOM lead scientist, and while relations with IOM were good, they did not lead to active collaboration.

Some international air pollution issues did, however, provide opportunities for active IOM involvement in epidemiological studies. Between 1995 and 2000, the Soufrière Hills volcano on the island of Montserrat erupted, forcing evacuation of the capital city, Plymouth, which was buried by lava and dust. Montserrat was and is an Overseas Territory of the UK and so the UK Department for International Development (DfID), with Maynard at DoH, commissioned an integrated set of research projects, including at IOM, to understand the risks to health. Much of the interest was on a form of silicon dioxide, cristobalite, within the volcanic ash, rather than the 'traditional' outdoor air pollutants. IOM research included exposure assessment studies led by Searl, toxicological studies in association with Donaldson and Seaton, and epidemiological studies led by Cowie of heavily exposed inhabitants who had remained on the island and of Montserratians who had been evacuated to the UK. While several detailed research reports were prepared,[97] the key results were summarised by Searl in a paper[98] with Cowie and Dr Peter Baxter from the University of Cambridge; while a more recent paper by Baxter, Searl, Cowie and others gives a very interesting account (part scientific report, part memoir) of the eruption and the associated health risk assessment.[99] Cristobalite in volcanic ash was found to be less toxic than previously thought. Results influenced DfID policy on how safe it was for evacuated islanders to return.

In a significant relatively new development, IOM is now also involved in epidemiological studies of air pollution in both China and India, in collaboration with the University of Edinburgh and others. This follows successful and effective work by a senior exposure scientist, Dr Miranda Loh, who has a particular interest in environmental issues and had won funding for this work from programmes of the UK Research Councils. Loh, then based at the national public health research institute KTL in Finland, had collaborated with IOM on a large EU-funded integrated project and had subsequently joined IOM after some years at the University of Arizona in the USA. Her work on air pollution in China and India has given new impetus and direction to IOM's wider involvement in air quality and health research.

Health risks from air pollution in other contexts

Health impact assessment of outdoor air pollution benefits from a uniquely strong research base, covering different kinds and concentrations of outdoor pollutants from various sources – traffic, industrial pollution, household burning of solid fuels. This, together with a surprising consistency in health risks estimated from different sources of particles (with relatively recent studies showing a consistency in risk across outdoor air pollution, second-hand tobacco smoke and active smoking),[100] greatly facilitates quantitative health impact assessment. But to what extent can this substantial body of knowledge be applied to airborne particles from other sources, for example indoors, or in underground transport systems?

This issue arose for IOM in the early 2000s when, following discussions at COMEAP, IOM was commissioned to carry out a study of the risks to health from exposure to dust in the London Underground railway system. Hurley, Cherrie and Dr Lang Tran, a highly able quantitative toxicologist at IOM (see chapter 7), collaborated with Seaton, Donaldson and others in an integrated set of exposure assessment and toxicology studies, designed to assess the risks to workers, but implicitly to the travelling public also. Again, the nature of the dust led to interesting issues of interpretation of risks. The dust levels were much higher than above ground owing to high levels of iron derived from brakes and track, but the numbers of very small (less than 0.1µm diameter) combustion particles were far lower. The study team's interpretation, based on understanding of the known consequences of iron-rich dust and of combustion particles, was that exposure to dust in the underground was probably less dangerous than similar exposures in the street above.[101] Suggestions of epidemiology to test this conclusion were not taken up.

More recently, similar issues arose in estimating risks to health from particulate pollution indoors in Scotland and Ireland, from burning of solid fuels indoors for cooking and heating, and from cigarette smoking indoors. Funded by the Irish Environmental Protection Agency and led by Dr Marie Coggins at the University of Galway, the work involved exposure assessment and health impact assessment, jointly also with the University of Aberdeen.[102] The HIA work, led by IOM, assumed that risk estimates from ambient particulate air pollution could also be applied to the particles from combustion indoors, thereby allowing assessment of a much wider set of risks to human health than would otherwise be possible.[103] It is fair to say that opinions differ on the validity of such an approach.

Environmental health impacts

IOM extended its experience in quantifying health impacts of outdoor air pollution, formed during ExternE and successor projects, into wider expertise on developing methods for environmental HIA and cost-benefit analysis (CBA). This culminated in 2007-12 in IOM, through Hurley, leading two major integrated assessment projects.

The EU-funded HEIMTSA, involving twenty-seven partners, included sub-projects led by IER Stuttgart, Imperial College London, the European Commission and the University of Thessaloniki, NILU in Norway, KTL in Finland, TNO in the Netherlands and Dr Alistair Hunt at the University of Bath. It developed a close working relationship with another major EU-funded integrated research project, INTARESE, led by Professor David Briggs at Imperial College. Very substantial methodological development did not fully see the light of day, as the projects struggled with a major case study of the environmental and health impacts of policies to reduce climate change. Perhaps its most accessible legacy is the awkwardly named Integrated Environmental Health Impact Assessment System (IEHIAS), with a wealth of useful information on conducting HIA in the context of environmental determinants of health.[104]

The second project, Environmental Determinants of Public Health in Scotland (EDPHiS) for the Scottish Government, involved collaboration with Professor George Morris and Dr Sheila Beck at NHS Health Scotland, with Dr Stefan Reis at CEH near Edinburgh, environmental and public health scientists from many Scottish universities, and others, to help understand how the environment affected children's health through asthma, obesity, unintentional injuries and mental health.[105] Cowie had a major role in both projects, as scientist and as scientific project manager, as had Susan Young: her effective administration and management of these complex multi-organisational projects was essential, as was practical support from Chris Owens (Commercial Director) and Dr Phil Woodhead (CEO) with the complexities of the financial arrangements.

Looking to the future

Through its work over the years, IOM now had an established presence on environment and health, and public health, in Scotland, in the UK and in Europe. HIA methods have by now become wellestablished, especially for outdoor air pollution and, while still an important focus of IOM work, with current collaborative projects on health impacts of air pollution in Thailand and on volcanic eruptions worldwide, the momentum on environmental research at IOM has moved to other developments, especially on modern methods of exposure assessment. One of these concerns the exposome, an all-embracing exposure concept and associated set of methodologies increasingly used to give coherence to exposure assessment. Cherrie and van Tongeren contributed to its development,[106] and IOM, through Loh and Cherrie, is a partner in HEALS,[107] a major EU-funded exposome project led by Professor Dimosthenes Sarigiannis at the University of Thessaloniki. The other is citizen science, where 'ordinary' citizens participate in measuring the environment and sharing data. IOM, through Hurley, Cowie, Galea and Dr Joanne Crawford, Head of Human Factors section, established a presence in this field through participation in the EU-funded project CITI-SENSE,[108] and other initiatives in Scotland. These initiatives are linked to the development and emergence into routine use of personal monitors for measuring air pollution, part of a wider movement of personalised environmental and medical measurement.

The recruitment in 2017 from Public Health England of Professor Sotiris Vardoulakis, one of the founders of the international Healthy Polis network, as Research Director (after van Tongeren left to succeed Agius as Professor of Occupational Health at Manchester University), gave new impetus and new directions to environment and public health as a research area at IOM. Despite the generally difficult climate of research funding in the UK, and possible difficulties with EU funding post-Brexit, there are still some opportunities for high-quality collaborative research on environment and public health, recognising also the integral links with social determinants of health. There is certainly a need, in an area where the benefits to human health of dependable knowledge, provided in a way that facilitates incorporation into the development of policy, far outweigh the costs of providing that evidence.

Chapter 5: References and Notes

1. Fay JWJ, Rae S. (1959). The Pneumoconiosis Field Research of the National Coal Board. *Annals of Occupational Hygiene*; 1: 149-161.

2. A confounder of a relationship between a possible cause of disease and the disease itself is some other characteristic, often another established or possible risk factor, which is related both to the possible causes being investigated and to the disease itself. In the present context, an individual's smoking history is a potential confounder in that it may be related to their dust exposure (for example, both may be related to age) and smoking is related to a range of lung diseases. Unless properly accounted for, a confounder is likely to distort the relationship being investigated.

3. Hurley JF, Alexander WP, Hazeldine DJ, Jacobsen M, Maclaren WM. (1987) Exposure to respirable coalmine dust and incidence of progressive massive fibrosis. *British Journal of Industrial Medicine*; 44: 661-672, which says that "In all, 53382 miners participated".

4. Figure 1 in Jacobsen (1979) reports that PFR1 included 31629 from twenty-four pits, plus 477 from a twenty-fifth: Jacobsen M. (1979). Vingt-six ans de recherches sur les pneumoconioses sur le terrain dans les charbonnages britanniques. Contribution de ces recherches à l'epidémiologie des affections pulmonaires des mineurs. *Revue de l'Institut d'Hygiéne des Mines*; 34: 203-216.

5. Oldham PD, Roach SA. (1952). A sampling procedure for

measuring industrial dust exposure. *British Journal of Industrial Medicine*; 9: 112-119.

6. Ashford JR. (1958). The design of a long-term sampling programme to measure the hazard associated with an industrial environment. *Journal of the Royal Statistical Society* (A); 121: 333-347.

7. Attfield MD, Kuempel ED. (2003). Pneumoconiosis, coalmine dust and the PFR. *Annals of Occupational Hygiene*; 47: 525–529.

8. Kromhout H. (2002). Design of measurement strategies for workplace exposures. *Occupational and Environmental Medicine*; 59: 349-54. In his review Kromhout, from the University of Utrecht in the Netherlands, says of the PFR: "It took more than 40 years to see such an effective measurement strategy being repeated and improved upon".

9. Hamilton R, Walton WH. (1961). The selective sampling of respirable dust. In: Davies CN, ed. *Inhaled Particles and Vapours*. Oxford: Pergamon Press: 465-483.

10. Hamilton RJ, Morgan GD, Walton WH. (1967). The relationship between measurements of respirable dust by mass and by number in British coalmines. In: Davies CN, ed. *Inhaled Particles and Vapours II*. Oxford: Pergamon Press: 533-548.

11. The laboratory analytical methods needed greater quantities of dust than were available from individual OGs.

12. Liddell FDK, Lindars DC. (1969). An elaboration of the ILO scale of simple pneumoconiosis. *British Journal of Industrial Medicine*; 26: 89-100. This simple idea, of how to refine a subjective ordered ranking scale, has wider value, well beyond the context of pneumoconiosis where it was initially developed.

13. For assessing relationships with dust exposure, what matters is that the film reader measures something meaningful (i.e. profusion of small opacities) in a consistent way. Where readers do measure with internal consistency, but one consistently records higher levels of disease (profusion)

than another, the two sets of readings in effect give different measuring instruments which can individually be related to dust exposure. IOM analyses for major studies were typically based on individual and summary results from five film readers, working independently.

14. A particular interest was to what extent classifications could be improved (i.e. differences between readers and differences in within-reader repeat classifications reduced) by having available to readers films selected by acknowledged experts as being typical of the *boundaries* between profusion categories rather than typical of the categories individually.

15. There was an urgency to have results, and so data from four collieries, surveyed late in the series and at the time not yet fully processed, were not included.

16. Jacobsen M, Rae S, Walton WH, Rogan J. (1970). New dust standards for British coal mines. *Nature*; 227: 445-447.

17. Jacobsen M, Rae S, Walton WH, Rogan JM. (1971). The relation between pneumoconiosis and dust exposure in British coal mines. In: Walton WH, ed. *Inhaled Particles III*. Old Woking (Surrey): Unwin Bros: 903-919.

18. This was a methodological breakthrough, largely unheralded at the time, but recognised clearly more recently – see Attfield and Kuempel, note 7, above.

19. Hurley JF, Burns J, Copland L, Dodgson J, Jacobsen M. (1982). Coalworkers' simple pneumoconiosis and exposure to dust at 10 British coalmines. *British Journal of Industrial Medicine*; 39: 120-127.

20. Soutar CA, Maclaren WM, Annis R, Melville AW. (1986). Quantitative relations between exposure to respirable coalmine dust and coalworkers' simple pneumoconiosis in men who have worked as miners but have left the coal industry. *British Journal of Industrial Medicine*; 43: 29-36.

21. Collins HP, Dick JA, Bennett JG, Pern PO, Rickards MA, Thomas DJ, Washington JS, Jacobsen M. (1988). Irregularly

shaped small shadows on chest radiographs, dust exposure, and lung function in coalworkers' pneumoconiosis. *British Journal of Industrial Medicine*; 45: 43-55.

22. Hurley JF. Dust-related risks of radiological changes in coalminers over a 40-year working life: report on work commissioned by NIOSH. Edinburgh, *Institute of Occupational Medicine*. (OOM Report TM 87/09).

23. Cowie HA, Hurley JF, Soutar CA, Pern P, Hutchison P. (1994). Further studies of progressive massive fibrosis (PMF) among miners and ex-miners. *Annals of Occupational Hygiene*; 38 (Supplement 1): 791-797.

24. Seaton A, Dick JA, Dodgson J, Jacobsen M. (1981). Quartz and pneumoconiosis in coalminers. *Lancet*; 2(8258): 1272-1275.

25. Jacobsen M, Maclaren WM. (1982). Unusual pulmonary observations and exposure to coalmine dust: A case-control study. *Annals of Occupational Hygiene*; 26: 753-765.

26. Miller BG, Hagen S, Love RG, Soutar CA, Cowie HA, Kidd MW, Robertson A. (1998). Risks of silicosis in coalworkers exposed to unusual concentrations of respirable quartz. *Occupational and Environmental Medicine*; 55: 52-58.

27. Buchanan D, Miller BG, Soutar CA. (2003). Quantitative relations between exposure to respirable quartz and risk of silicosis. *Occupational and Environmental Medicine*; 60: 159-164.

28. Soutar CA, Miller BG, Hurley JF, Cowie HA, Buchanan D. (2004). Dust concentrations and respiratory risks in coalminers: key risk estimates from the British Pneumoconiosis Field Research. *Occupational and Environmental Medicine*; 61: 477-481.

29. Rogan JM, Attfield MD, Jacobsen M, Rae S, Walker DD, Walton WH. (1973). Role of dust in the working environment in development of chronic bronchitis in British coalminers. *British Journal of Industrial Medicine*; 30: 217-226.

30. Rae S, Walker DD, Attfield MD. (1971). Chronic bronchitis and dust exposure in British coalminers. In: Walton WH, ed. *Inhaled Particles III*. Old Woking, Surrey: Unwin: 883-895.

31. While miners with pneumoconiosis typically had lower lung function (given age, height and smoking status), this was because of their generally higher dust exposures and not because of the presence of pneumoconiosis as such; i.e. lower lung function was related to CWP when CWP was a surrogate measure of exposure, but not otherwise.

32. Love RG, Miller BG. (1982). Longitudinal study of lung function in coal-miners. *Thorax*; 37: 193-197.

33. Soutar CA, Hurley JF. (1986). Relation between dust exposure and lung function in miners and ex-miners. *British Journal of Industrial Medicine*; 43: 307-320.

34. Cowie HA, Miller BG, Soutar CA. (1999). Dust-related clinically relevant lung functional defects. Edinburgh: *Institute of Occupational Medicine*. (IOM Report TM/99/06).

35. Jacobsen M, Smith TA, Hurley JF, Robertson A, Roscrow R. (1988). Respiratory infections in coal miners exposed to nitrogen oxides. Research Report of the Health Effects Institute. 18: 1-56.

36. Robertson A, Dodgson J, Collings P, Seaton A. (1984). Exposure to oxides of nitrogen: respiratory symptoms and lung function in British coalminers. *British Journal of Industrial Medicine*; 41: 214-219.

37. Hurley JF, Soutar CA. (1986). Can exposure to coalmine dust cause a severe impairment of lung function? British Journal of Industrial Medicine; 43: 150-157.

38. Marine WM, Gurr D, Jacobsen M. (1988). Clinically important effects of dust exposure and smoking in British coal miners. *American Review of Respiratory Disease*; 137: 106-112.

39. Coggon D, Newman Taylor A. (1998). Coal mining and chronic obstructive pulmonary disease: a review of the evidence. *Thorax*; 53: 398-407.

40. Miller BG, Jacobsen M. (1985). Dust exposure, pneumoconiosis, and mortality of coalminers. *British Journal of Industrial Medicine*; 42: 723-733.

41. This is what is known as the 'Healthy Worker Effect' – workers, especially manual workers, must be relatively fit to secure and to keep in employment. See e.g. Fox AJ, Collier PF. (1976). Low mortality rates in industrial cohort studies due to selection for work and survival in the industry. *British Journal of Preventive & Social Medicine*; 30: 225-230.

42. Miller BG, MacCalman L. (2010). Cause-specific mortality in British coal workers and exposure to respirable dust and quartz. *Occupational and Environmental Medicine*; 67: 270-276.

43. Jacobsen J. (2018). Defending the data. *Significance*; 15: 18-23. Available at https://rss.onlinelibrary.wiley.com/doi/epdf/10.1111/j.1740-9713.2018.01189.x

44. Hurley JF, Archibald RML, Collings PL, Fanning DM, Jacobsen M, Steele RC. (1983). The mortality of coke workers in Britain. *American Journal of Industrial Medicine*; 4: 691-704. doi: 10.1002/ajim.4700040603.

45. Hurley JF, Cherrie JW, Maclaren WM. (1991). The mortality of coke workers in Britain: a 20-year follow-up. Edinburgh: *Institute of Occupational Medicine*. (IOM Report TM/91/01).

46. Miller BG, Doust E, Cherrie, Hurley JF. (2013). Lung cancer mortality and exposure to polycyclic aromatic hydrocarbons in British coke oven workers. *BMC Public Health*; 13: 962.

47. Jacobsen M, Collings PL, Fanning DM, Hurley JF, Steele RC. (1982). Mortality of workers in the British steel and coke industries. Final report on CEC contracts No 7246-24/8/001 and 7246.24.009. Edinburgh: Institute of Occupational Medicine. (IOM Report TM/82/06).

48. Hutchison PA, Cowie HA, Donnan PT, Hurley JF, Taylor CF, Pilkington A. (1996). Mortality of British Steel workers over an extended follow-up period. Edinburgh: Institute of Occupational Medicine. (IOM Report TM/96/06).

49. Miller BG, Donnan PT, Sinclair A, Edwards JC, Soutar CA, Hurley JF. (1996). The respiratory and cardiovascular health of iron and steel process workers. Part II: results of the field

studies and of the analyses of the data. Edinburgh: Institute of Occupational Medicine. (IOM Report TM/96/05).

50. This involved study design, cohort sampling and identification, development of study methods, medical surveys of workers, gathering of data on work histories, smoking histories and other factors, measurement of dust concentrations, data verification and collation, statistical analysis, interpretation.

51. Collaboration is essential, for example, in getting agreement from both management and unions, identifying workers for study, getting co-operation for medical field work on-site, classifying jobs in relation to dust and other conditions, carrying out a dust sampling programme, and estimating dust conditions historically.

52. Soutar CA, Copland L, Thornley PE, Hurley JF, Ottery J, Adams WG, Bennett B. (1980). Epidemiological study of respiratory disease in workers exposed to polyvinyl chloride dust. *Thorax*; 35: 644-652.

53. Graham MK, Cowie HA, Miller BG, Cherrie JW, Hurley JF, Hutchison PA. (2005). Mortality study of workers at the Hillhouse PVC plant. Edinburgh: Institute of Occupational Medicine. (IOM Report TM/05/05).

54. Seaton A, Lamb D, Brown WR, Sclare G, Middleton WG. (1981). Pneumoconiosis of shale miners. *Thorax*; 36: 412-418.

55. Miller BG, Cowie HA, Middleton WG, Seaton A. (1986). Epidemiologic studies of Scottish oil shale workers: III. Causes of death. *American Journal of Industrial Medicine*; 9: 433-446.

56. Seaton A, Louw SJ, Cowie HA. (1986). Epidemiologic studies of Scottish oil shale workers: I. Prevalence of skin disease and pneumoconiosis, and Louw SJ, Cowie HA, Seaton A. II. Lung function in shale workers' pneumoconiosis. *American Journal of Industrial Medicine* 9: 409-421 and 423-432.

57. Randall SC. (1990). Studies of the Scottish oil shale industry. Vol.1: A socio-historical study of Scottish shale mining communities in Mid- and West Lothian, Final report on US

Department of Energy Agreement no.DE-AC02-84ER66199. Edinburgh: Institute of Occupational Medicine. (IOM Report TM/90/02).

58. Mark D, Vincent JH. (1986). A new personal sampler for airborne total dust in workplace. *Annals of Occupational Hygiene*; 30: 89-102.

59. Love RG, Smith TA, Gurr D, Soutar CA, Scarisbrick DA, Seaton A. (1988). Respiratory and allergic symptoms in wool textile workers. *British Journal of Industrial Medicine*; 45: 727-741.

60. Love RG, Muirhead M, Collins HP, Soutar CA. (1991). The characteristics of respiratory ill health of wool textile workers. *British Journal of Industrial Medicine*; 48: 221-228.

61. Love RG, Waclawski ER, Maclaren WM, Wetherill GZ, Groat SK, Porteous RH, Soutar CA. (1999). Risks of respiratory disease in the heavy clay industry. Occupational and Environmental Medicine; 56: 124-133.

62. Davies LST, Robertson A, Agius RM, Cowie HA, Cherrie JW, Hutchison P. (1994). The use of compliance monitoring for assessing quarry workers' exposures to respirable dust and quartz. *Annals of Occupational Hygiene*; 38 (Supplement): 559-570.

63. Agius RM , Love RG , Davies LST , Hutchison PA , Cherrie JW , Robertson A , Cowie HA , Hurley JF , Seaton A , Soutar CA. (1992). Epidemiological studies of respiratory health and dust exposure in hard rock quarry workers and ex-workers. Edinburgh: *Institute of Occupational Medicine*. (IOM Report TM/92/10).

64. Love RG, Miller BG, Groat SK, Hagen S, Cowie HA, Johnston PP, Hutchison PA, Soutar CA. (1997). Respiratory health effects of opencast coalmining: a cross-sectional study of current workers. Occupational and Environmental Medicine; 54: 416-423.

65. The sampling seemed inefficient, in measuring dust concentrations in parts of the operation where clearly there was no dust problem – but it was important for exposure estimation in the research to have estimates of dust concentrations for all

OGs, not just the high-concentration ones. And the sampling seemed of poor quality, because the work done by individuals being sampled was not tracked as company people would have done – but the research focus was, correctly, on OG average concentrations, not the detail of tasks underlying each and every individual sample.

66. Cowie HA, Wild P, Beck J, Auburtin G, Piekarski C, Massin N, Cherrie JW, Hurley JF, Miller BG, Groat S, Soutar CA. (2001). An epidemiological study of the respiratory health of workers in the European refractory ceramic fibre industry. *Occupational and Environmental Medicine*; 58: 800-810.

67. In the late 1980s, concern was expressed in the media and among agricultural workers of farmers and others suffering acute symptoms and long-term neurological illness after dipping sheep with organophosphate pesticides. It was of particular interest to establish whether long-term illness could occur even if there had been no severe acute response immediately following dipping.

68. Pilkington A, Buchanan D, Jamal GA, Gillham R, Hansen S, Kidd M, Hurley JF, Soutar CA. (2001). An epidemiological study of the relations between exposure to organophosphate pesticides and indices of chronic peripheral neuropathy and neuropsychological abnormalities in sheep farmers and dippers. *Occupational and Environmental Medicine*; 58: 702-710.

69. Galea KS, MacCalman L, Jones K, Cocker J, Teedon P, Cherrie JW, van Tongeren M. (2015). Comparison of residents' pesticide exposure with predictions obtained using the UK regulatory exposure assessment approach. *Regulatory Toxicology and Pharmacology*; 73: 634-643. doi: 10.1016/j. yrtph.2015.09.012.

70. Miller BG, Colvin AP, Hutchison PA, Tait H, Dempsey S, Lewis D, Soutar CA. (2008). A normative study of levels of uranium in the urine of British Forces personnel. *Occupational and Environmental Medicine*; 65: 398-403.

71. Galea K, Cherrie JW. (2010). Report on a historical hygiene assessment at National Semiconductor (NSUK). Web published: Health and Safety Executive. (Report 884-0010). http://www.hse.gov.uk/statistics/pdf/hha2010.pdf

72. Darnton A, Miller BG, MacCalman L, Galea KS, Wilkinson S, Cherrie JW, Shafrir A, McElvenny D, Osman J. (2012). An updated investigation of cancer incidence and mortality at a Scottish semiconductor manufacturing facility with case-control and case-only studies of selected cancers. *Occupational and Environmental Medicine*; 69: 767-769. http://dx.doi.org/10.1136/oemed-2011-100606.

73. Van Tongeren M, Jimenez AS, Hutchings SJ, MacCalman L, Rushton L, Cherrie JW. (2012). Occupational cancer in Britain. Exposure assessment methodology. *British Journal of Cancer*. 107 (Suppl 1): S18-26.

74. Rushton L, Hutchings SJ, Fortunato L, Young C, Evans GS, Brown T, Bevan R, Slack R, Holmes P, Bagga S, Cherrie JW, van Tongeren M. (2012). Occupational cancer burden in Great Britain. *British Journal of Cancer*: 107 (S1), S3-S7. doi:10.1038/bjc.2012.112.

75. Cherrie JW, Hutchings S, Gorman Ng M, Mistry R, Corden C, Lamb J, Sánchez Jiménez A, Shafrir A, Sobey M, van Tongeren M, Rushton L. (2017). Prioritising action on occupational carcinogens in Europe: a socioeconomic and health impact assessment. *British Journal of Cancer*; 117: 274–281. doi:10.1038/bjc.2017.161.

76. Agius RM, Lloyd MH, Campbell S, Hutchison PA, Seaton A, Soutar CA. (1994). Questionnaire for the identification of back pain for epidemiological purposes. *Occupational and Environmental Medicine*; 51: 756-760.

77. Waclawski ER, Hagen S, Symes AM, Graveling RA, Scott AJ, Miller BG. (1993). Case control study of the relations between risk of back pain sickness absence and the nature of tasks carried out by coalminers. Final report on CEC research

contract 7280/04/022. Edinburgh: Institute of Occupational Medicine. (IOM Report TM/93/05).

78. Tesh K, Tigar F, Graveling RA, Hagen S, Lorenzo S, Ritchie P, Hutchison P. (1995). Pregnancy and lifting. Final report on HSE contract SC/89 42/247/1. Edinburgh: Institute of Occupational Medicine. (IOM Report TM/95/02).

79. Hanson MA, Donnan PT, Graveling RA, McLaren WM, Butler MP, Hurley JF, Kidd MW, Lancaster RJ, Prescott CA, Symes AM, Tesh KM. (1999). Epidemiological and ergonomic study of occupational factors associated with syndromes of upper limb disorders in keyboard operators. Edinburgh: Institute of Occupational Medicine. (IOM Report TM/99/04).

80. Cowie HA, Miller BG, Rawbone RG, Soutar CA. (2006). Dust related risks of clinically relevant lung functional deficits. *Occupational and Environmental Medicine*; 63: 320-325.

81. Health and Safety Executive. SART Prototype Tool. Available at: http://www.hse.gov.uk/sicknessabsence/sart/index.htm

82. Ayres JG, Boyd R, Cowie H, Hurley JF. (2011). Costs of occupational asthma in the UK. *Thorax*; 66: 128-133.

83. External costs are the costs imposed on others, without compensation, when producing or consuming goods and services. In the present context they are the costs to individuals and society of damage to the environment, including resultant damage to human health, when producing electricity or using transport.

84. ExternE is the well-known acronym for 'External Costs of Energy' and a synonym for a series of projects from the early 90s to 2005 – http://www.externe.info/externe_d7/–which also lists the key partners (including IOM) who developed the methodology and some of the numerous projects where it has been applied.

85. Department of Health. (1995). Committee on the Medical Effects of Air Pollutants. *Non-biological Particles and Health*. London: HMSO. For most *individuals* most of the time the

risks are not great; but because everybody is exposed, the overall *public health effects*, which range from minor cardio-respiratory conditions through to hospital admissions and earlier deaths, can be very large.

86. IOM's work was greatly helped by parallel work in the USA led by Dr Bart Ostro of the California Environmental Protection Agency (EPA), by help from some established air quality and health scientists in Europe, notably Professor Bert Brunekreef in the Netherlands, and by participation in various advisory or working groups on air pollution and health, notably COMEAP (Committee on the Medical Effects of Air Pollutants) in the UK, and by ExternE colleagues like Ari Rabl at Armines in France and Mike Holland, then at AEA Technology in England. But main development and overall responsibility was IOM's.

87. Berry J, Holland M, Watkiss P. (1995). Externalities of Energy. "ExternE" Project. Volume 2. Luxembourg: European Commission. http://www.externe.info/externe_d7/sites/default/ files/vol2.pdf, especially chapter 4: Public health effects of air pollution arising from fossil fuel combustion: 61-156.

88. For a more recent list, see http://www.externe.info/externe_ d7/?q=node/56

89. Searl A, Hurley F, Holland M, King K, Stedman J, Vincent K. (2003). Quantifying the health impacts of pollutants emitted in Central Scotland. Web published: Scottish Executive. https:// www2.gov.scot/resource/doc/1052/0002242.pdf

90. Holland M, Berry J, Foster D. (1999). ExternE. Externalities of Energy. Volume 7. Methodology 1998 update. Luxembourg: European Commission. http://www.externe.info/externe_d7/ sites/default/files/vol7.pdf and Bickel P, Rainer F. (2005). ExternE. Externalities of Energy. Methodology 2005 update. Luxembourg: European Commission. http://www.externe.info/ externe_d7/sites/default/files/methup05a.pdf

91. See http://ec.europa.eu/environment/archives/cafe/activities/ cba.htm, especially AEA Technology Environment. (2005).

Methodology for the cost-benefit analysis for CAFE: Volume 2: Health impact assessment. Didcot: AEA Technology Environment, where IOM are main authors: http://ec.europa. eu/environment/archives/cafe/pdf/cba_methodology_vol2. pdf. The CAFE cost-benefit analysis work was led by Paul Watkiss at AEA Technology Environment in England, with a central team of Watkiss, Hurley, Mike Holland, formerly AEA and by then an independent consultant, and Alistair Hunt, a senior environmental economist at the University of Bath.

92. Miller BG, Hurley JF. (2003). Life table methods for quantitative impact assessments in chronic mortality. *Journal of Epidemiology & Community Health*; 57: 200-206.

93. https://www.iom-world.org/research/our-expertise/iomlifet/ includes a description of IOMLIFET and free downloads.

94. COMEAP. (2010). The mortality effects of long-term exposure to particulate air pollution in the United Kingdom. Chilton, Didcot: Health Protection Agency. https://assets.publishing.service.gov.uk/ government/uploads/system/uploads/attachment_data/file/304641/ COMEAP_mortality_effects_of_long_term_exposure.pdf

95. Associations of long-term average concentrations of nitrogen dioxide with mortality (2018): COMEAP summary. https://www. gov.uk/government/publications/nitrogen-dioxide-effects-on-mortality/associations-of-long-term-average-concentrations-of-nitrogen-dioxide-with-mortality-2018-comeap-summary

96. Reference (i) HRAPIE report: WHO. (2013). Health risks of air pollution in Europe – HRAPIE project. Recommendations for concentration-response functions for cost-benefit analysis of particulate matter, ozone and nitrogen dioxide. Copenhagen: World Health Organization; and (ii) Anenberg SC, Belova A, Brandt J, Fann N, Greco S, Guttikunda S, Heroux ME, Hurley F, Krzyzanowski M, Medina S, Miller B, Pandey K, Roos J, Van Dingenen R. (2016). Survey of ambient air pollution health risk assessment tools. *Risk Analysis*. 36: 1718-36. doi: 10.1111/ risa.12540.

97. (i) Searl A, Nicholl A, Baxter PJ. (2002). Assessment of the exposure of islanders to ash from the Soufrière Hills volcano, Montserrat, British West Indies. *Occupational and Environmental Medicine*; 59: 523-531. (ii) Cowie HA, Graham MK, Searl A, Miller BG, Hutchison PA, Swales C, Dempsey S, Russell M. (2002). A health survey of workers on the island of Montserrat. Edinburgh: Institute of Occupational Medicine. (IOM Report TM/02/02).

98. Searl AS, Baxter PJ, Cowie HA. (2002). Exposure to volcanic ash on Montserrat, British West Indies. *Annals of Occupational Hygiene*; 46 (Suppl 1): 35-38.

99. Baxter PJ, Searl AS, Cowie HA, Jarvis D, Horwell CJ. (2014). Evaluating the respiratory health risks of volcanic ash at the eruption of the Soufrière Hills Volcano, Montserrat, 1995 to 2010 (Chapter 22). In: Wadge G, Robertson REA, Voight B, eds. *The Eruption of Soufrière Hills Volcano, Montserrat from 2000 to 2010.* London: Geological Society. 39: 407-425.

100. Pope CA, Burnett RT, Turner MC, Cohen A, Krewski D, Jerrett M, Gapstur SM, Thun MJ. (2011). Lung cancer and cardiovascular disease mortality associated with particulate matter exposure from ambient air pollution and cigarette smoke: shape of the exposure-response relationships. *Environmental Health Perspectives*; 119: 1616-1621. doi:10.1289/ehp.110363921768054.

101. Seaton A, Cherrie J, Dennekamp M, Donaldson K, Hurley JF, Tran CL. (2005). The London Underground: dust and hazards to health. *Occupational and Environmental Medicine*; 62: 355-362.

102. Coggins MA, Semple S, Hurley F, Shafrir A, Galea KS, Cowie H, Sánchez Jiménez A, Garden C, Whelan P, Ayres JG. (2013). Indoor Air Pollution and Health (IAPAH) (2008-EH-MS-8-S3) STRIVE Report. Johnstown Castle, Co Wexford: Environmental Protection Agency. http://epa.ie/pubs/reports/research/health/indoor%20air%20pollution%20and%20health%20(iapah)_final%20report.pdf

103. Galea KS, Hurley JF, Cowie H, Shafrir AL, Sánchez Jiménez A, Semple S, Ayres JG, Coggins M. (2013). Using PM2.5 concentrations to estimate the health burden from solid fuel combustion, with application to Irish and Scottish homes. *Environmental Health*; 12: 50, 19 June (epub).

104. IEHIAS. Integrated Environmental Health Impact Assessment System. http://www.integrated-assessment.eu/eu/indexf5d0. html?q=guidebook/about_iehias

105. Environmental Determinants of Public Health in Scotland (EDPHiS). http://www.edphis.org.uk/

106. Van Tongeren M, Cherrie J. (2012). An integrated approach to the exposome. *Environmental Health Perspectives*; 120(3): A104. (Letter).

107. Sargiannis DA. (2018). The HEALS Project. In: Dagnino S, Macherone A, eds. *Unravelling the Exposome. A Practical View*. New York: Springer. Chapter 16.

108. CITI-SENSE. http://www.citi-sense.eu/

6

How much and what kinds of exposure cause disease?

Summary

Measurement of the exposure of workers to harmful substances, either in epidemiological studies or for other purposes, has been a core skill for IOM through all its research. Early pioneering work was undertaken within the PFR programme and this has influenced the exposure science in many later epidemiological studies. New methods of measuring dust and airborne asbestos fibres developed by IOM exposure scientists have been adopted as standard approaches throughout the world, most notably the IOM inhalable dust sampler and the Walton-Beckett microscope eyepiece graticule.

In the course of a major European research project in the synthetic fibre manufacturing industry, new mathematical modelling approaches to estimate historic workplace exposures have been developed; this knowledge has been applied subsequently to produce modelling tools to estimate human exposure for European chemical regulation. IOM scientists have also undertaken pioneering work on measurement of skin exposure and inadvertent ingestion exposure in workplaces, and IOM is one of the main international centres of expertise in these aspects of exposure science. In addition to investigating how people are exposed, IOM scientists have had a strong interest in evaluating the effectiveness of protective measures such as respirators and face masks.

Continuing innovation and response to new challenges as medical understanding expands has been an important aspect of IOM research. This is illustrated by recent research into the assessment of exposure to sub-concussive head trauma for a study of the neurological health of professional footballers.

Exposure to airborne dust

Exposure science, which aims to identify and characterise uptake into the body of toxic materials, has always been at the core of IOM's work. The PFR project, described in detail in chapters 1 and 5, set out to identify how much and what kinds of dust caused lung disease in coal miners. To do this it was necessary to know the average concentration of dust inhaled by each miner throughout the many years of the study. To gather this information researchers were stationed at each of the collieries to collect samples of airborne dust in close proximity to the workers. Of course, it was impracticable to sample every miner on every work shift and so a strategy was devised to enable representative samples to be obtained, which could be used to estimate the exposure of each worker.

Drs James Fay and Stewart Rae, two scientists working on the PFR, devised an innovative system where the workforce was divided into different 'occupational groups', comprising men doing the same job, at the same place, at the same time.[1] Workers were then selected at random from these groups to be sampled throughout their work shift, including the time travelling to and from their underground workstations. Time worked in each occupational group was recorded in the research to enable an estimate of the cumulative amount of dust exposure to be calculated. This approach was to form the basis for most occupational epidemiological studies carried out subsequently as it provides an efficient way of characterising the exposure of large groups of workers. Around 50,000 men were included at least once in the PFR study and in the first seven years of the research more than 14,000 shifts were sampled, with around 60,000 individual exposure measurements being made. At its peak, around a hundred scientists and technicians were involved in this effort.

Respirable dust

When the PFR study started, the best technique available to collect samples of the fine dust that was inhaled and retained in the deep lung was the thermal precipitator. This is a rather cumbersome device that required an investigator to collect, repeatedly over a few minutes, samples of the airborne dust onto glass slides for later microscopic evaluation in the laboratory [fig 6.1]. In the laboratory, using an optical microscope that magnified the image 2,500 times, the technician then had to count individual particles between 0.5 and 5 µm diameter; these are the particles (defined as respirable) considered to be most relevant to coal workers' pneumoconiosis, being most likely to be inhaled deep into the

Fig 6.1: A thermal precipitator being used to
collect a dust sample in a British coal mine

lung. A major problem with the process was the subjectivity involved in a technician counting the dust particles, which initially resulted in average differences between individuals of more than two to one. To control for these errors, it was necessary to have an elaborate training and quality assurance scheme involving all the technicians regularly counting the same samples.[2] Even so, the results were still subject to high variability and for the PFR to be successful it was necessary to devise a new approach.

The key IOM scientist involved in improving the sampling methods for the PFR was Henry Walton (see chapter 1). Walton had worked as a physicist at the government chemical and biological research centre at Porton Down during World War II, and then had joined the National Coal Board and then IOM. He was the driving force behind revolutionising the dust sampling by moving away from microscopic analysis of the particles to the direct collection of respirable dust in sufficient quantities to enable the sample to be weighed and the concentration to be expressed in gravimetric terms as the mass of dust in milligrams per cubic metre of air (mg/m^3). Walton's innovation, along with his colleague Bob Hamilton, was to realise that the finer respirable dust fell more slowly in air, and by arranging for the sampled air to flow along narrow channels between parallel plates it was possible to select the particles that corresponded to those reaching the area of the lungs where oxygen is taken up and where the dust could cause pneumoconiosis. The instrument they devised was the MRE 113A sampler, which became the basis for the standard method of collecting airborne dust samples in mines in Britain and many other parts of the world[3] [fig 6.2]. The idea of sampling only the fraction of airborne dust inhaled into the part of the lungs where disease was caused was revolutionary and has influenced all subsequent approaches to assessing the health risks from dusts.

Early analyses of the association between the exposure of miners in the PFR, as determined by particle counting, and the severity of pneumoconiosis showed only a weak link. However,

Fig 6.2: The MRE 113A respirable dust sampler

when the researchers used exposure measures based on gravimetric estimates there was a strong correlation, and this data analysis was the subject of IOM's first landmark scientific paper published in *Nature* in 1970.[4]

When IOM was founded in 1969, exposure science was in its infancy. In 1953 the British Occupational Hygiene Society (BOHS) had been formed, with Walton, Hamilton, Cyril Jones, who worked on the PFR study in South Wales, and Dr John Rogan as founder members. Ultimately, both Rogan and Walton became Presidents of the Society, along with several other IOM scientists. The BOHS established a scientific journal, *Annals of Occupational Hygiene*,[5] and inaugurated an influential series of Symposia on Inhaled Particles. Henry Walton had a key role in both, and many of IOM's early research findings were published in the journal or in the proceedings of the symposia. The motto of the BOHS, *'Felix, qui potuit rerum cognoscere causas'*, from *Georgics* by the Latin poet Virgil (70–19 BC) – happy he who could understand the causes of things, reflected its scientific interests.

Inhalable dust

IOM's interest in aerosol sampling in coal mines continued, recognising a need to be able to sample accurately the larger airborne particles that might be associated with diseases, such as chronic bronchitis, in the upper airways of the lung. To do this the researchers focused on those particles that could enter the nose and mouth of a dummy head under different environmental wind conditions and compared the sampling characteristics of the human head to different sampling instruments. The work was undertaken by three young physicists, Dr Trevor Ogden, Len Birkett and Harry Gibson. They found that as the particle diameters increased the proportion that entered the nose or mouth decreased, until at around 10 to 15 m, only around 40% of the particles in the air were inhaled [fig 6.3].

None of the existing samplers investigated was satisfactory to measure this fraction of the airborne dust, so they developed a new 47mm filter holder – the Orb sampler – which imitated the sampling characteristics of the human head in wind speeds up to 2.75 m/s and particle diameters up to 25 μm.

Fig 6.3a: The Orb inhalable sampler (see ref 35)

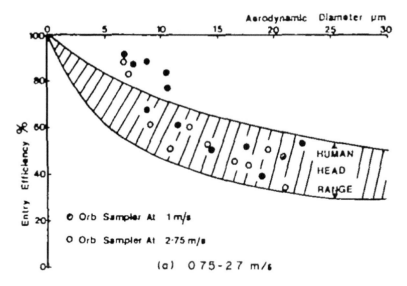

Fig 6.3(b): The sampling characteristics compared to the human head

Henry Walton retired from IOM in 1978, but only after he had recruited the physicist Dr Jim Vincent to continue the work on aerosol science. Vincent, along with Drs Dave Mark, Rob Aitken and others, further developed the concept of the inhalable dust fraction which was eventually established as an international convention and was adopted in workplace exposure measurement regulation and guidance worldwide. The team developed and patented a range of practical sampling devices, in particular the IOM personal inhalable sampler,[6] which can be used to collect airborne dust samples on individual workers over the whole duration of a work shift [fig 6.4]. This sampler, produced under licence by SKC (a rare example of IOM commercialising a product), is widely recognised as most appropriate for measurement of the inhalable fraction and is used daily in workplaces across the world. The inhalable function and the IOM personal inhalable sampler have become the global standard method for measuring occupational exposure to dusts, and which are now written into European and International Standards.

Fig 6.4: The IOM personal inhalable sampler

IOM staff have continued to use the skills and knowledge from this earlier research in new situations, for example, in developing methods for measuring exposure to coke oven particulate matter, later used in a study to understand the lung cancer risk for those working in that industry.[7] Other applications included measurement of particle exposures in the London Underground railway system to determine whether there were any health risks to workers or the travelling public from exposure to tunnel dust,[8] and particle exposure of Scottish bar workers over a twelve-month period before and after the introduction of Scottish smoke-free legislation to evaluate its effectiveness. This latter study showed the new laws to have been associated with about a 90% reduction in passive smoke exposure among those working in the industry.[9]

Asbestos

With the endowment of the Asbestosis Research Foundation at IOM in 1971 (chapter 1), there was an increasing interest in methods for measuring asbestos fibres in the air. During the 1960s, small battery-operated pumps had been used to draw air through membrane filters held in a plastic holder. In 1971 the British asbestos manufacturing industry, through its Asbestosis Research Council, published a method for measuring airborne asbestos using this 'membrane filter' method. The method was relatively simple and once sampling was complete the filters were chemically treated to make them transparent. They were then examined through a high-powered optical microscope to count the number of fibrous particles on a small part of the filter. The count could then be used to calculate the concentration of fibres in the sampled air.[10] Henry Walton and a young scientist, Dr Steve Beckett, realised that to count the fibres reliably it was necessary to have a defined area on the magnified image and to provide appropriate scale marks to determine the size of the particles. They invented a microscope graticule, that is optically superimposed on the image to assist the counting process.[11] [fig 6.5]

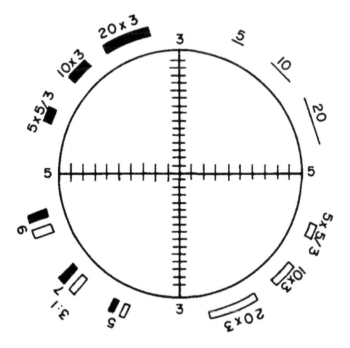

Fig 6.5: The Walton-Beckett microscope graticule

This graticule was quickly adopted as a standard part of the asbestos fibre counting methodology and it continues to be used throughout the world. This and other research at IOM helped to produce an internationally agreed method for measuring asbestos fibres using phase contrast optical microscopy, published by the World Health Organization (WHO). Key staff involved with this work were Drs Nigel Crawford, Alan Jones, Arthur Johnston, with Cherrie and Vincent.

Experience in the PFR study had shown the problems with assessment of airborne particles using microscopic counting; different technicians could get widely different results. The same was likely to be true of asbestos fibre counting. Beckett and statistician Dr Mike Attfield arranged a series of interlaboratory comparisons by exchanging prepared samples that were evaluated by each participating laboratory.[12,13] The average differences between laboratories was as expected large, up to a factor of four, but differences between individual technicians could be even larger. In 1979 IOM was appointed as the UK's Central Reference Laboratory for asbestos fibre counting with the aim of standardising this analysis. IOM scientists worked closely with the Health and Safety Executive and the Asbestosis Research Council to come up with a suitable quality assurance scheme for laboratories undertaking this type of work, and in 1984 the Regular Interlaboratory Counting Exchanges (RICE) scheme was launched (see chapter 3).[14] The RICE scheme improved greatly the reliability of data produced by UK laboratories, there eventually being more than 300 participant organisations. In parallel, IOM set up an international quality assurance scheme for asbestos fibre counting known as the Asbestos Fibre Regular Informal Counting Arrangement (AFRICA), and while this scheme had fewer member laboratories they were drawn from around fifteen countries, including Brazil, South Africa, Colombia and Italy. These schemes were important tools to help ensure more reliable measurements of worker exposure around the world.

Synthetic fibres

From the mid-1980s, IOM collaborated with the International Agency for Research on Cancer (IARC) in a major European epidemiological study of the carcinogenicity of mineral wool fibres and other synthetic mineral fibres (previously known by several names including 'man-made mineral fibres'). IOM's expertise in measuring airborne dust in large epidemiological studies was key to this collaboration. The World Health Organization (WHO) appointed IOM as its Central Reference Laboratory for man-made mineral fibre counting, a similar role to the one in the UK for asbestos, and IOM scientists also developed a standard method for WHO for measuring airborne synthetic mineral fibres.

Cherrie, Jim Dodgson, John Ottery, George Harrison and colleagues were responsible for surveys of airborne fibre concentrations in each of thirteen synthetic mineral fibre factories throughout Europe. These investigations showed that workers in this industry were generally exposed to low fibre concentrations, but there were more deaths from lung cancer than would have been expected if the workers had been representative of the general population of the countries involved in the study. There were nagging doubts amongst the scientists involved in the research that in the past the conditions in the factories had been much worse than were found during the surveys, as illustrated by the two photographs [fig 6.6].

Cherrie and Dodgson carried out a historical investigation in the plants and found that during the early phase of the technology the fibre concentrations had almost certainly been higher than in modern production, and they were able to define in each factory when these technological changes took place.[15] An epidemiological analysis using these data concluded that in the factories that produced fibre from rock or metal slag materials the lung cancer risk in the early phase may have been increased due to high fibre exposure, either alone or in combination with other exposures.[16] No increased risk was found in the factories that used

Fig 6.6:
Photographs
from European
mineral wool
manufacturing
plants in the
1930s and 1980s

glass to make fibres but it was suspected that these fibres were less persistent after being inhaled into the lungs.

Ten years after the initial studies, a reanalysis of the mortality experience of the same workers, when almost twice as many had died, showed the same results, and the researchers embarked on a more intensive investigation of the possible reasons for the increased deaths from lung cancer. As part of this work IOM helped develop novel methods to estimate retrospectively the exposures of workers in the study.[17] This research demonstrated that there was no evidence of a carcinogenic effect of these fibres on the lung, the association being with the very high smoking habits of the workers in the early times, some of whom had smoked more than 400kg of tobacco during their lives.[18] This important reversal of the original conclusions was based firmly on the exposure assessments carried out by IOM. The results have been influential in the development of international regulations for the use of synthetic fibres and were a key element of the decision by the WHO International Agency for Research on Cancer to downgrade the carcinogenicity classification for these materials.

IOM scientists, led by Fintan Hurley, also conducted a study of the respiratory health of workers manufacturing refractory ceramic fibre in Europe, showing small, although inconsistent, effects on respiratory health associated with exposure to these fibres.[19] This was in a small group of workers employed in making a very specialised type of synthetic mineral fibre and it was impractical to explore their mortality in an epidemiological study. However, it was possible to carry out toxicological studies on these and other fibres (see chapter 7).

Modelling exposures

The experience in developing methods to reconstruct past exposure for epidemiological studies promoted an interest amongst IOM's researchers in using modelling approaches in other circumstances, particularly for use by chemical regulatory agencies and exposure scientists in industry. Cherrie and Graeme Hughson carried out an investigation of the reliability of the exposure model used by the European Union to evaluate whether chemicals could be sold on the market, known as the Estimation and Assessment of Substance Exposure (EASE) tool.[20] This evaluation showed that EASE had poor accuracy and was in fact little better than a random selection of exposure category. Clearly this was an inadequate tool for chemical regulation and with the introduction of new legislation on chemicals in Europe, the Registration, Evaluation and Authorisation of Chemicals (REACH) Regulations, it became imperative to develop new assessment tools.

IOM teamed up with scientists at the Health and Safety Executive in Britain, TNO in the Netherlands and others in Europe to develop a new approach, one based on IOM's methods for reconstructing past exposure in epidemiological studies. This led to the development of the Advanced REACH Tool or ART.[21] At its core this is a sophisticated tool for estimating inhalation exposure to a wide range of chemicals, using information about the circumstances of exposure combined with any available measurement data. It is now widely used and is approved by the European Chemicals Agency (ECHA) for use within REACH. The basis of the ART model has also been used to help estimate worker inhalation exposure to pharmaceutical agents, and to provide a basis for identifying workers who have been exposed to asbestos to assess whether they should undergo screening to detect respiratory cancers.[22,23] It is probably one of the most reliable generic exposure estimation tools that has been produced.

It is important to understand how exposure changes when interventions are made to protect workers, and the modelling approach provides a way to assess these impacts. However, it is also possible to use longitudinal measurement datasets to identify how exposures change over time. Drs Karen Galea, Martie van Tongeren and others reviewed the published literature to identify and analyse these types of long-term trends.[24] They found a general downward trend, with on average around a 5-10% change each year and that this was true for dusts, gases or fibres wherever around the world the measurements had been made [fig 6.7]. These declines seem to be an almost universal trend and are reassuring, suggesting that workplace conditions are generally improving, levels typically halving every decade.

Van Tongeren led a team that has evaluated other model tools that have been approved by ECHA for exposure assessment under REACH; these are known as 'lower-tier' tools and are simpler than ART and expected to be less accurate.[25] To overcome the accuracy problem and still provide a valid assessment they are

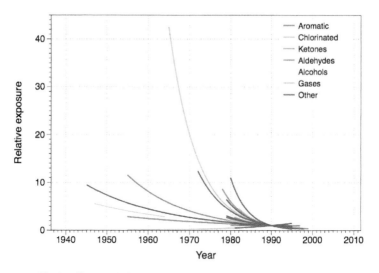

Fig 6.7: Temporal changes for gas and vapour exposure over time

designed to overestimate the true exposure. Van Tongeren's study is the most comprehensive evaluation of the performance of REACH exposure tools carried out to date. Although generally conservative, the tools do not always achieve the performance specified in the REACH guidance. These results have prompted improvements by the tool developers that will help ensure the safety of workers using chemicals at work; constructive suggestions have been made to improve these types of tool by providing better training and support for users.

IOM's work on developing and evaluating exposure models has been scientifically important and makes an important contribution to evaluating the safety of chemicals in Europe and beyond.

Skin and ingestion exposure
Much of IOM's recent research on chemical exposure has been focused on exposure measurement studies for regulatory risk assessment, under REACH and the predecessor regulatory

systems but, led by Cherrie, IOM has also had a prominent role in developing techniques for measuring skin exposure of workers. Studies in relation to metals, including dermal exposure to nickel, zinc and lead, have been carried out together with work on the measurement of exposure to oil mist aerosol and vapour for offshore oil workers and exposure of workers to heavy fuel oils.

Estimation of historical skin exposures of farmers dipping sheep in pesticide solutions, for an epidemiological study led by Dr Adele Pilkington, proved particularly challenging. However, this research demonstrated a strong association between concentrated organophosphate (OP) pesticides in the dip and neurological symptoms amongst the workers, although a less consistent association with other health measures.[26] As a consequence of this research, the UK Government withdrew these pesticides from the market until safer handling systems were devised. In collaboration with scientists from the Health and Safety Laboratory, IOM carried out the world's largest investigation of possible exposures of bystanders and people living close to agricultural land where pesticides had been sprayed.[27] This involved collecting urine samples from residents soon after spraying events and at other times during the year and, reassuringly, showed that the exposures were no higher after pesticides were sprayed than at other times.

Cherrie and Dr Alastair Robertson came up with a novel idea for a sampling instrument to measure dermal exposure to chemicals and new theoretical models to help understand how skin exposure may arise. These instruments and models may in the future help provide more reliable assessments of the risks from chemicals to the skin. Cherrie and colleagues also devised a method to measure the amount of water on the skin of the hand as a measure of the risk of dermatitis from wet-work, wet hands being one of the main causes of irritant dermatitis.[28] This method has been used in a small number of research studies and has helped provide a better understanding of the risks from this type of work.

The interest in the chemical contamination of skin has led IOM to investigate the potential for workplace exposure from inadvertent ingestion of chemicals by hand-to-mouth contacts and other pathways.[29] A theoretical model integrating both ingestion and dermal uptake has been used to investigate the importance of specific factors in determining transfer to the mouth, and a simple model to estimate the contribution of exposure from inadvertently ingesting material has been developed. Interestingly, individual behavioural factors such as nail biting and the tendency to touch the face were key determinants of exposure. Much of this work was carried out by Drs Melanie Gorman-Ng and Yvette Christopher, with supervision from Dr Sean Semple and van Tongeren.

IOM scientists have led the development of these new exposure measurement approaches to help ensure that we can assess the safety of chemicals in workplaces and in use by consumers.

Protecting workers and others from harmful exposures

In addition to investigating how people get exposed, IOM scientists have had a strong interest in evaluating the effectiveness of protective measures such as respirators and face masks. Early work was concerned with the effectiveness of respirator usage in coal mines and in coke ovens. This work prompted Robin Howie and others to develop a powered helmet respirator that would be suitable for use in coal mines. This device was based around a hard-hat that protected the head from knocks and bumps, with a small fan located in the helmet to blow air through a filter and down in front of the face. Although the research produced promising results the devices were never commercialised. However, the concept has found wide acceptance in other industries.

Additionally, IOM has had an interest in evaluating the performance of respirators in real-life work situations. This was because the standard tests that are carried out to approve respirators are undertaken in a prescriptive way in a controlled laboratory environment. Experience shows that when people wear respirators in workplaces, they seldom do this in the optimal way. Cherrie, Howie and Robertson investigated the reliability of simple disposable masks used in DIY activities at home.[30] Most of the masks tested were inadequate, some were very uncomfortable to wear, and most manufacturers provided no information to the wearer. In this case, it was found that the introduction of a standard test would probably result in the development of better, more comfortable and effective masks.

An important piece of research was the assessment of the effectiveness of high-efficiency respiratory protective equipment for asbestos removal work.[31] This involved measuring the concentration of asbestos inside and outside the respirator while men were working with asbestos-containing materials. The concentrations measured outside the respirator in these situations were hundreds, sometimes thousands, of times higher than are now permitted and so the effectiveness of the respirators was very important. This work was done in the 1990s and this way of working would certainly be completely unacceptable these days. The workers had all been trained, but the researchers did not require them to wear the respirators in the best way, so the results are a realistic assessment of the effectiveness of the protection routinely achieved. The results from this study are shown [fig 6.8]: each point represents a measurement from a person wearing a respirator, with the horizontal axis showing the concentration outside the respirator and the vertical axis shows the concentration inside the mask being inhaled by the worker.

While most of the measurements were above the present-day legal limit for asbestos fibre concentrations in air (0.1 fibres/ml), only three of the in-mask concentrations were above the limit. These results are reassuring, suggesting that these high-efficiency respirators can provide good protection for the wearers.

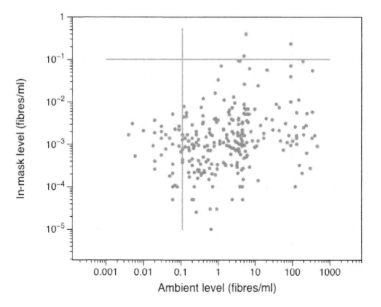

Fig 6.8: Comparison of the asbestos fibre
concentration inside and outside the respirator

Recently, evaluations of disposable respirators and other face masks were included in two studies: one investigated the possible protection of people from air pollution in cities in China and the second from volcanic ash during and after an eruption.[32, 33] This work was led by Dr Miranda Loh and involved Will Mueller, Susanne Steinle, Andrew Apsley and others. These studies showed that although a mask may be made from an effective filter material it does not necessarily translate into an effective device, the seal between the mask and the face being key to getting an effective reduction in exposure. Makeshift masks made from handkerchiefs, bandanas or shawls were completely ineffective, and the best-performing masks were commercial devices sold for use in workplaces. The information from this research has been incorporated into international guidance that is used by aid agencies and governments when planning public health protection measures. There has been widespread interest in the effectiveness of face masks to protect the general public from air pollution, and several newspaper and magazine articles have been published describing IOM's research.

Increasingly IOM is applying the exposure science expertise of its staff in epidemiological projects on the health effects of environmental air pollution. Cherrie has been leading a study of the health impact of pollutants in Thailand, which involves exposure monitoring and measurements inside and outside the homes of subjects, and Loh leads work in Beijing and Delhi. All these projects involve collaborations with local researchers and engagement with those involved in health protection activities in the country.

Conclusions and prospects

IOM's exposure science research has changed as the scientific challenges have changed. The initial efforts to develop new sampling instruments and methods of measuring exposure have continued as a constant theme throughout its fifty years, from the inhalable dust sampler, through to pioneering new approaches to measure skin and inadvertent ingestion exposure to chemicals. New methodologies that rely on simple low-cost sensors along with monitoring of a wide range of biomarkers in blood and urine are continuing to be developed. These techniques aim to measure the "exposome", the totality of exposures from conception to death, which if it can be achieved, will complement measurements of the genome and provide a more complete explanation of the causes of disease.

IOM's exposure research is fully multidisciplinary, relying on physicists, chemists, biologists, psychologists and ergonomists, and collaboration with researchers working throughout the world. The future will throw up different challenges: current work includes methods to assess lifetime exposure to sub-concussive head trauma for a study of neurological health of professional footballers and methods to evaluate whether wearing a face mask reduces the effects of particulate air pollution using measurements of a range of health biomarkers. Measurement and assessment of exposure to toxic agents in the workplace and the wider environment and protection from such exposure remain central to the on going research at IOM.

Chapter 6: References and Notes

1. Mike Attfield, a statistician who worked on the PFR before going to work for NIOSH in the USA, and Eileen Kuempel wrote a reflective commentary on the importance of the PFR for occupational exposure assessment. Attfield MD, Kuempel ED. (2003). Pneumoconiosis, coalmine dust and the PFR. *Annals of Occupational Hygiene*; 47: 525-529.

2. Holdsworth JF, Price FH, Tomlinson RC. (1954). Inter-laboratory checks on the counting of coal dust particles on thermal precipitator slides. *British Journal of Applied Physics*; 5: S96-S100.

3. The Mines Research Establishment (MRE) sampler was developed by Hamilton and Walton. Key papers in this development were Walton WH. (1954). Theory of size classification of airborne dust clouds by elutriation. *British Journal of Applied Physics* 5 (S3): S29-S37 and Hamilton RJ, Walton WH. (1961). The selective sampling of respirable dust. *Inhaled Particles and Vapours* 25: 213–36. Hamilton R, Walton WH. (1961). The selective sampling of respirable dust. *Inhaled Particles and Vapours* 25, 213–236. doi:10.1080/00028896409342581.

4. Jacobsen M, Rae S, Walton WH, Rogan JM. (1970). New dust standards for British coal mines. *Nature*; 227: 445-447.

5. Now known as the *Annals of Work Exposures and Health* (https://academic.oup.com/annweh), the journal continues to thrive and is still one of the main places where IOM scientists publish their research findings.

6. Mark D, Vincent JH. (1986). A new personal sampler for airborne total dust in workplaces. *Annals of Occupational Hygiene*; 30: 89-102.

7. Miller BG, Doust E, Cherrie JW, Hurley JF. (2013). Lung cancer mortality and exposure to polycyclic aromatic hydrocarbons in British coke oven workers. *BMC Public Health*; 13: 962. doi:10.1186/1471-2458-13-962.

8. Seaton A, Cherrie J, Dennekamp M, Donaldson K, Hurley JF, Tran CL. (2005). The London Underground: dust and hazards to health. *Occupational and Environmental Medicine*; 62: 355-362. doi:10.1136/oem.2004.014332.

9. Semple S, MacCalman L, Naji AA, Dempsey S, Hilton S, Miller BG, Ayres JG. (2007). Bar workers' exposure to second-hand smoke: the effect of Scottish smoke-free legislation on occupational exposure. *Annals of Occupational Hygiene*; 51: 571-580. doi:10.1093/annhyg/mem044.

10. Holmes S. (1965). Developments in dust sampling and counting techniques in the asbestos industry. *Annals of the New York Academy of Sciences*; 132: 288-297.

11. Walton WH, Beckett S. (1977). A microscope eyepiece graticule for the evaluation of fibrous dusts. *Annals of Occupational Hygiene*; 20: 19-23.

12. Beckett ST, Attfield MD. (1974). Inter-laboratory comparisons of the counting of asbestos fibres sampled on membrane filters. *Annals of Occupational Hygiene*; 17:85-96. doi:10.1093/annhyg/21.1.85.

13. Walton WH, Attfield M, Beckett S. (1976). An international comparison of counts of airborne asbestos fibres sampled on membrane filters. *Annals of Occupational Hygiene*; 19: 215-224.

14. Crawford N, Brown P, Cowie A. (1992). The RICE and AFRICA Schemes for asbestos fibre counting. *Annals of Occupational Hygiene*; 36: 59-69. doi:10.1093/annhyg/36.1.59.

15. Cherrie J, Dodgson J. (1986). Past exposures to airborne fibres and other potential risk factors in the European man-made mineral fibre production industry. In: Saracci R, ed. Contributions to the IARC study on mortality and cancer

incidence among man-made mineral fiber production workers. Helsinki: Institute of Occupational Health: 1986: 26-33 (*Scandinavian Journal of Work, Environment and Health*; 12 (supp1.1)).

16. Simonato L, Fletcher AC, Cherrie J, Andersen A, Bertazzi PA, Charnay N, Claude EJ, Dodgson J, Esteve J, Frentzel-Beyme R, Gardner MJ, Jensen OM, Olsen JH, Olsen H, Saraccil R, Teppo L, Winkelmann R, Westerholm P, Winter PD, Zocchetti C. (1986). The man-made mineral fiber European historical cohort study: extension of the follow-up. In: Saracci R, ed. Contributions to the IARC study on mortality and cancer incidence among man-made mineral fiber production workers. Helsinki: Institute of Occupational Health, Finland: 34-47 (*Scandinavian Journal of Work, Environment and Health*; 12 (suppl.1)).

17. Cherrie J, Schneider T. (1999). Validation of a new method for structured subjective assessment of past concentrations. *Annals of Occupational Hygiene*; 43: 235-245.

18. Kjærheim K, Boffetta P, Hansen J, Cherrie J, Chang-Claude J, Eilber U, Ferro G, Guldner K, Olsen JH, Plato N, Proud L, Saracci R, Westerholm P, Andersen A. (2002). Lung cancer among rock and slag wool production workers. *Epidemiology* 13: 445-453.

19. Cowie HA, Wild P, Beck J, Auburtin G, Piekarski C, Massin N, Cherrie JW, Hurley JF, Miller BG, Groat S, Soutar CA (2001). An epidemiological study of the respiratory health of workers in the European refactory ceramic fibre industry. *Occupational and Environmental Medicine*; 58: 800-810.

20. Cherrie J, Hughson GW. (2005). The validity of the EASE expert system for inhalation exposures. *Annals of Occupational Hygiene*; 49: 125-134.

21. Tielemans E, Schneider T, Goede H, Tischer M, Warren N, Kromhout H, Fogh CL. (2008). Conceptual model for assessment of inhalation exposure: defining modifying factors.

Annals of Occupational Hygiene; 52: 577–586. doi:10.1093/annhyg/men059.

22. Cherrie JW, Gillies AT, Sleeuwenhoek A, van Tongeren M, McDonnell P, Coggins M, Bailey SR. (2009). Modelling exposure to pharmaceutical agents. *Journal of Physics: Conference Series*; 151: 012063. doi: 10.1088/1742-6596/151/1/012063.

23. Cherrie JW, McElvenny D, Blyth KG. (2017). Estimating past inhalation exposure to asbestos: A tool for risk attribution and disease screening. *International Journal of Hygiene and Environmental Health*; 1-0. doi:10.1016/j.ijheh.2017.09.013.

24. Creely KS, Cowie H, van Tongeren M, Kromhout H, Tickner J, Cherrie J. (2007). Trends in inhalation exposure: a review of the data in the published scientific literature. *Annals of Occupational Hygiene*; 51:665-678. doi:10.1093/annhyg/mem050.

25. Van Tongeren M, Lamb J, Cherrie JW, MacCalman L, Basinas I, Hesse S. (2017). Validation of lower tier exposure tools used for REACH: Comparison of tools estimates with available exposure measurements. *Annals of Work Exposures and Health*; 1-18. doi:10.1093/annweh/wxx056.

26. Pilkington A, Buchanan D, Jamal G, Gillham R, Hansen S, Kidd M, Hurley JF, Soutar CA. (2001). An epidemiological study of the relations between exposure to organophosphate pesticides and indices of chronic peripheral neuropathy and neuropsychological abnormalities in sheep farmers and dippers. *Occupational and Environmental Medicine*; 58: 702-710.

27. Galea KS, MacCalman L, Jones K, Cocker J, Teedon P, Cherrie JW, van Tongeren M. (2015). Comparison of residents' pesticide exposure with predictions obtained using the UK regulatory exposure assessment approach. *Regulatory Toxicology and Pharmacology*; 1-61; doi:10.1016/j.yrtph.2015.09.012.

28. Cherrie J, Apsley A, Semple SE. (2007). A new sampler to assess dermal exposure during wet working. *Annals of Occupational Hygiene*; 51:13-18. doi:10.1093/annhyg/mel059.

29. Cherrie J, Semple S, Christopher Y, Saleem A, Hughson GW, Philips A. (2006). How important is inadvertent ingestion of hazardous substances at work? *Annals of Occupational Hygiene*; 50: 693-704. doi:10.1093/annhyg/mel035.

30. Cherrie J, Howie RM, Robertson A. (1987). The performance of nuisance dust respirators against typical industrial aerosols. *Annals of Occupational Hygiene*; 31: 481-491.

31. Howie RM, Johnstone JBG, Weston P, Aitken RJ, Groat S. (1996). Workplace effectiveness of respiratory protective equipment for asbestos removal work. Sudbury: HSE Books. (HSE Contract Research Report No. 112/1996).

32. Cherrie JW, Apsley A, Cowie H, Steinle S, Mueller W, Lin C, Horwell CJ, Sleeuwenhoek A, Loh M. (2018). Effectiveness of face masks used to protect Beijing residents against particulate air pollution. *Occupational and Environmental Medicine*; 75: 446-452. doi:10.1136/oemed-2017-104765.

33. Steinle S, Sleeuwenhoek A, Mueller W, Horwell CJ, Apsley A, Davis A, Cherrie JKW, Galea KS. (2018). The effectiveness of respiratory protection worn by communities to protect from volcanic ash inhalation. Part II – Total inward leakage tests. *International Journal of Hygiene and Environmental Health* 221: 977-984. doi:10.1016/j.ijheh.2018.03.011.

34. Roach SA. (1959). Measuring dust exposure with the thermal precipitator in collieries and foundries. *British Journal of Industrial Medicine*; 16: 104-122.

35. Ogden TL, Birkett JL. (1978). An inhalable-dust sampler, for measuring the hazard from total airborne particulate. *Annals of Occupational Hygiene*; 21: 41-50.

From coal and asbestos to nanoparticles: contributions to pathology and toxicology

Summary

Pathology, the study of the structural and functional features of disease, was an important part of the early research programme in IOM. It started with studies of the lungs of coal miners who had participated in the PFR, and was able to answer the critical questions about the inter-relations of dust exposure, pneumoconiosis and chronic obstructive pulmonary disease, showing that coal dust exposure was a risk factor for emphysema, a critical component of the latter. This work also helped to define the causes of the different radiological appearances of pneumoconiosis and to differentiate the effects of quartz and coal exposure.

Alongside this human pathology was a programme of respiratory toxicology, a study of how inhaled substances might harm the lungs. Initial experimental work on dust inhalation in rats moved, as time passed, into more basic studies of cellular and immunological responses to dust. Studies of asbestos fibres defined the physical characteristics of a dangerous fibre in terms of length, diameter and solubility in the lung, and this important understanding led to a means of assessing the potential toxicity of other fibrous substitutes for asbestos. Studies of dusts previously regarded as non-toxic showed that they might overload defence mechanisms in the lung, leading to an important conceptual advance in toxicology based on the surface area of dust particles rather than the mass. This became of critical importance in understanding the toxic properties of nanoparticles.

As key researchers moved to academic posts, they continued to develop these ideas in collaboration with IOM scientists, helping to explain the cardiac effects of air pollution and to develop the new science of nanotoxicology, leading to IOM's major interest in nanosafety.

The coal studies

The history of understanding coal miners' diseases had demonstrated the importance of obtaining data on two things in particular: the miners' longevity and causes of death, and the pathological changes in their lungs. Both were taken account of in the early planning of the PFR and accepted by both trade unions and management. The former required permission to obtain the death certificates of as many deceased miners as possible who had been studied while they were still at work; the PFR has been described in detail in chapter 5. The latter required permission to be sought for autopsy examinations of as many participants as possible after their deaths, with removal of their lungs for further study. The crucial nature of this research had been demonstrated between the 1930s and 1970s by the work of two professors in the Cardiff Medical School, Stevenson Lyle Cummins and Jethro Gough,[1] and was to play a critical role in the IOM research programme.

To obtain the lungs required not only the agreement of the miners themselves and their relatives, but also of the pathologists working in the various coal mining areas. This was facilitated by coal workers' pneumoconiosis (CWP) being a formally reportable disease, a characterisation that required doctors to report such deaths to coroners or, in Scotland, the Procurators Fiscal. As time passed, this agreement was honoured more in the breach than the observance; nevertheless, sufficient lungs were obtained through this pathway. At the same time, invaluable help was provided by the National Union of Mineworkers in publicising in mining areas the value of autopsies to the research in benefiting the health of future miners.

Dr John Davis had been recruited from Cambridge University where he had been Director of Research in the Pathology Department. He had been using the new weapon in the armoury of experimental pathologists, the electron microscope, to study the extreme detail of the interaction between asbestos fibres and tissue that leads to disease. His brief was to lead a pathology branch that addressed research questions related to the mechanisms of pathology caused by coal and other particle types. His primary interest was in experimental pathology, and he received key support in the coal studies first from Dr Ann le Roux and later from Dr Anne Ruckley, Dr June Fernie, Joe Chapman and Andy Douglas, with overall supervision by Dr David Lamb of the University of Edinburgh's Pathology Department. The unique strength of this research was that every lung studied was linked to data, obtained from the man in the course of the PFR, of his symptoms, smoking habit, lung function, chest radiographic appearances and, crucially, his exposure to coal dust during his working life. Categorisation of the pathological appearances could thus be linked to these data and, also, to data on the amount of dust, including minerals such as quartz and silicates, found in the lung. Less satisfactorily, many of the lungs were not well inflated and rather difficult to study in sufficient detail. In total, 490 suitable lungs were available for examination and a series of important publications flowed from these studies. These reflected the interest in relating the radiological or physiological findings to the amount and types of pneumoconiosis and the amount of emphysema in the lungs.

Different pathological changes reflected exposures to different types of coal. Exposures to high-rank coal (that with high carbon content) caused pigmented lesions and when progressive massive fibrosis (PMF) had occurred it had apparently developed from enlargement of a single lesion. In contrast, low-rank coals caused lesions that looked less dusty and, in some cases, resembled silicotic nodules [figs 7.1 and 7.2].[2] It seems likely that in men exposed to low-rank coal dust, while the overall risk of pneumoconiosis is low, if the dust contains significant amounts of quartz silicosis may occur.[3]

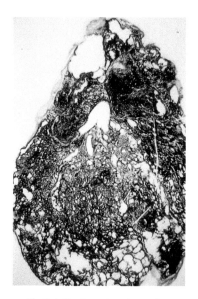
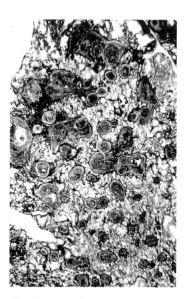

Fig 7.1: Post-mortem lung slice showing PMF in upper zone and emphysema in lower zone

Fig 7.2: Lung slice showing silicotic nodules coalescing into PMF at the top

The type of lesion in the lung related to the amount of dust retained in it. High-rank coal exposure was associated with higher dust content, smaller sized nodules on the radiograph, and more emphysema [fig 7.3]. Lower-rank coal was associated with less dust, and the radiographic profusion was mainly related to the silicates in the lung rather than the coal content. High silica exposures were associated with larger nodules on radiography.[4]

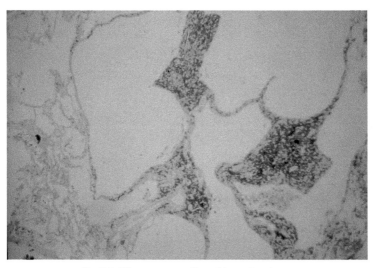

Fig 7.3: Microscope section of lung showing a
coal macule surrounded by emphysema

In men with pathological evidence of pneumoconiosis, the risk of significant emphysema was related to the dust content of the lung and the exposure of the individual. This was crucial evidence that emphysema, the most important pathological feature of chronic obstructive pulmonary disease and thus the main cause of impaired lung function, could be caused by coal dust exposure. This study also showed that the risk of emphysema in such cases was lower if there was a relatively high exposure to quartz, suggesting that competing adverse effects towards fibrosis and emphysema were occurring.[5]

The profusion of radiological opacities related to the number of lesions found in the lungs and to the lung dust content, particularly in men whose x-ray film showed the small opacities categorised as p and q.[6] At the time there was much interest in the physiological effects, if any, of different sized lesions on miners' radiographs.

These results complemented the parallel results of the epidemiological studies discussed in chapter 5. The response of the lungs to coal dust is to react both to remove it and to reduce its toxicity, but in this process the equivalent of a scar may be formed and this inflammatory reaction itself may harm the lung leading to both pneumoconiosis and emphysema to differing degrees. Carbon in coal is itself harmful, particularly if the coal is of high rank, but less high-quality coals contain quartz and silicates which, especially the former, may cause another form of pneumoconiosis, silicosis. And in general, the more dust a man is exposed to and retains in his lungs, the higher his risk. The epidemiological studies were designed to quantify these risks.

The asbestos studies

At the time of the foundation of IOM, diseases due to asbestos were of rapidly increasing medical and public health interest. Asbestosis, a fibrosis or scarring of the lungs in asbestos workers, causing breathlessness and usually death, had been known since the early 20th century and from 1950 it had been recognised that people with this disease had a significantly high additional risk of lung cancer. Then, in 1960, another fatal malignant disease, mesothelioma, was described among asbestos workers in South Africa, many of whom did not have asbestosis. It was becoming apparent that this effect of exposure could occur at relatively low doses and differed between different types of asbestos. The problems confronting government regulators in preventing these diseases while asbestos continued to be used and workers continued to be exposed were considerable. Importantly, asbestos was a very useful commodity that gave strength to materials such as cement, and insulated buildings and ships against fire; it was very widely dispersed in the built environment and in hundreds of applications in machines, so that workers were being exposed not only in manufacture of products, but also in repair and demolition of buildings and machinery such as railway trains and boilers. So long as people were being exposed, it was necessary to have information on how best to protect them. Short of banning the material and its use, this required:

*   Knowledge of how best to measure asbestos in the air
*   Knowledge of the exposures necessary to cause the different diseases
*   Understanding of the differences in toxicity between different types of asbestos

At the time there was a genuine scientific dispute on the harmfulness of asbestos with respect to the causation of lung cancer and mesothelioma, the commonest type (white asbestos or chrysotile) being thought by some to be relatively much less dangerous in this respect. Understanding the determinants of toxicity would have implications also with respect to substitute materials such as glass and ceramic fibres that were being introduced. Ultimately, human epidemiology provided answers, but IOM's work was to concentrate on experimental studies in rats and on standardising the measurement of asbestos in air.

It is important to recognise that this work on asbestos was funded by a consortium of companies involved in asbestos production and use, under the title of the Asbestosis Research Council (ARC). Initially the contract did not explicitly state that IOM was free to publish its results, but from 1978 the IOM Director, Dr Anthony Seaton, obtained this guarantee in the annual contracts. While at no time had publication been prevented, ARC controlled the overall direction of the research and were never persuaded to fund epidemiology at IOM, despite proposals to do so.

Experimental pathology and toxicology

Asbestos exposure studies

By the late 1960s it was well documented that inhaling asbestos fibres in workplaces caused both cancer and scarring of the lung, and Davis and his colleague Dr Rob Bolton undertook a series of experimental pathology studies to explore the main factors leading to these effects. There are three industrially important types of asbestos – amosite (brown asbestos), crocidolite (blue asbestos) and chrysotile (white asbestos) – and they seemed to cause disease to differing extents; it remained unknown what physicochemical characteristics of the fibres drove the differences in pathogenicity. The concept that the toxicity of particles is related to their physicochemical structure – the so-called structure/toxicity relationship – is the central thread that ran through all these studies. Indeed, this may be seen as the overarching objective of all the experimental pathology and toxicology of particles that was carried out both at IOM and elsewhere. Elaborating this relationship between structure and pathogenicity was not only of theoretical interest; it had multiple valuable uses in providing the optimum metric that should be used to measure exposure, understanding underlying cellular toxicity, developing predictive short-term testing to replace long-term animal experiments and, most importantly, developing strategies to prevent disease.

Davis and Bolton initiated a series of studies that were highly influential in defining the relationship between fibre structure and toxicity. In the early studies the ability of the experimental rat model to mimic human pathogenic responses to inhaled asbestos was demonstrated, with scarring, cancer of the lungs and cancer in the pleural lining of the lung (mesothelioma) developing. However, exposure to asbestos by inhalation produced the pleural tumour, mesothelioma, in a very low proportion of animals. In order to investigate the effect directly on the affected tissue, the pleura or peritoneum, an injection model that was a sensitive indicator of potential to produce mesothelioma, was developed by Bolton.[7]

The determinants of toxicity of asbestos

The next projects related to the roles of the three main structural factors of asbestos fibres, namely, their length, thickness and solubility/durability, the latter eventually being termed biopersistence to emphasise that solubility in the lung was what was important. These complex experimental pathology questions were addressed using exposure of rats, in purpose-built Perspex chambers, to highly defined clouds of fibres for seven hours a day, five days a week to mimic human exposure in the workplace. Carrying out these exposures was a very specialised task, requiring aerosol physicists to prepare fibres with a defined-length distribution, specialists in aerodynamics to carry out rigorous monitoring to control the consistency of the cloud over months and even years of exposure, and trained animal technicians. Physicists involved in the early studies were Drs Steve Beckett and Alan Jones. The greatest care was taken to protect IOM staff from exposure to asbestos themselves from the beginning of these experiments.

The outcome of these studies was key to demonstrating the relationship between fibre characteristics and pathology. Early studies showed that only very thin fibres were able to cause disease, confirming reports that thicker fibres do not gain access to the deeper parts of the lungs. The issue of fibre length was addressed in a very influential study using amosite asbestos. One sample, enriched for long fibres, was compared to the same sample of long fibres that had been ground down to short fibres. The length of the inhalation exposure period and the airborne concentration ensured that approximately similar masses of long and short fibre preparation accumulated in the lungs of the two groups of rats. Remarkably, virtually no pathological change developed in the animals exposed to the short fibres whereas a large proportion of animals exposed to the long fibres developed lung cancer and severe scarring.[8] A sister study using long and short white asbestos showed a similar effect of fibre length.[9] These

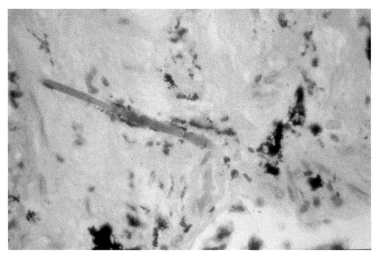

Fig 7.4: An asbestos fibre that has reached the deep lung but is too
long to have been removed and has caused fibrosis

studies gave the clearest demonstration of the importance of fibre
length as a toxicity factor; length is now accepted to be one of the
defining characteristics of a harmful fibre [fig 7.4].

The studies with white asbestos also highlighted the
importance of biopersistence. Fibres that dissolve in the lungs
are of course not available to mediate long-term damage. White
asbestos is soluble in the lungs, and Davis early recognised the
role of biopersistence in reducing the toxicity of white in relation to
blue and brown types.[10] Fibre biopersistence, diameter and length
are now seen as the three structural factors that imbue an asbestos
fibre with pathogenicity. The outcome of these early studies
was therefore that long, thin, biopersistent asbestos fibres were
recognised as the harmful entity and that as thickness, shortness
and solubility increased, fibres were rendered less harmful. This
knowledge had obvious implications with respect to assessing
toxicity of substitute fibres (see Synthetic vitreous fibres, below).

Cell biology studies

Long-term animal experiments such as those described above, whilst vital at the outset and indeed 'state of the art' in the 1960-80s era, were soon being recognised as problematic from both animal welfare and cost perspectives. Increasing understanding of the basic pathobiological processes involved in cancer and scarring in the lungs in other contexts was advancing apace. These new insights uncovered endpoints that could be assessed in short-term assays to understand the pathological impact of dusts without waiting for a rat's entire two- to three-year lifespan and seeing actual pathology. Thus, the notion that short-term testing might yield the information that was needed regarding structure versus toxicity and cellular/molecular mechanisms of particle and fibre pathogenicity began to take hold. To this end Seaton, who was an honorary consultant physician at Edinburgh's City Hospital, obtained use of two buildings known as cottages, in the grounds of the hospital. Several of these had been used for isolation of fever patients but with changes in disease patterns had become redundant. Dr Pat Gormley, a structural geneticist and cell biologist, had been appointed to lead the research in 1974, and a small group started using cellular approaches to address the toxicology of dusts. In these early studies the focus was on coal mine dust, and human and rat cell cultures were exposed to dust in culture dishes. But these were early days and the only assays available were limited to measuring cell death and certain enzymes; these formed the output from the early studies. It proved difficult to relate these rather non-specific endpoints to a complex disease like pneumoconiosis, but these were nevertheless among the first short-term studies performed to investigate pathogenicity.[11]

In 1984 Dr Ken Donaldson took over as Head of the Cell Biology Unit. He had previously come to IOM as a pathology technician but had been awarded a scholarship by the NCB to study at Stirling University, where he had obtained a first-class honours degree. He brought back with him knowledge of the remarkable advances that had taken place in understanding the cellular, though not yet molecular, mechanisms of disease consequent upon deposition of particles and fibres in lungs. These studies led to his obtaining his PhD from Edinburgh University. Central to them was the recognition that the triggering of an inflammatory response was key and that this could be investigated using the new technique of bronchoalveolar lavage that was then becoming widespread to understand the cell biology. A milestone European-funded study was carried out to assess the inflammatory potential of a range of colliery dusts, with quartz and titanium dioxide (TiO_2) as positive and negative controls respectively,[12] obtaining fluid from the lungs of rats following short-term inhalation exposure. These showed that colliery dusts caused more inflammation than TiO_2, a remarkably benign dust provided it is not present at very high doses (overload – see Low-toxicity dust, below). Importantly, these studies supported the PFR epidemiological findings that quartz had no role in the inflammation-causing effects of colliery dusts at the proportions of quartz exposure commonly found in UK coal mines, that is below about 10% of the total dust concentration.[13]

These findings kick-started a generation of research on the mechanisms whereby particle structure was related to the activity of inflammation and formed the backbone of subsequent studies on various particle types.[14] As an example, Dr Geraldine Brown worked on the ability of cells obtained from the lungs of rats that had inhaled coal mine dust over the short term to initiate lung damage by inflammation.[15] These were found to be many times more toxic than similar cells that had not been exposed to dust, thereby suggesting a mechanism for the damage to the lungs in coal miners with scarring or emphysema. As time progressed these approaches became more sophisticated in order to progress to an understanding of the dust-induced lung diseases in molecular terms.

Aspergillus fumigatus

Early observations by Seaton on the spores of the soil fungus *Aspergillus fumigatus* were the basis of the only substantial non-dust-related research into lung disease undertaken in the pathology branch at that time. He had described that these spores, which are found ubiquitously in the air, were able to survive in the lungs whilst other spores were killed by the cells that defend the lung, the macrophages. This squared with the well-documented finding that, in the lungs of some immune-compromised individuals and people with asthma, this fungus may cause serious disease, unlike most other fungal spores that are inhaled in the ambient air. The IOM studies led by Dr Maura Robertson, originally a pathology technician who obtained her PhD from this work, revealed that the spores of *A. fumigatus* release a soluble substance that stuns the defence cells such that they cannot ingest or kill these spores as they do with other common fungal spores.[16] The aspergillus spores had most likely evolved this mechanism to give them an advantage in the soil, where single-celled organisms, such as amoebae, use them as food.[17] Unfortunately for humans, this ability of spores being able to survive longer in soil also enables them to survive in the lungs, protecting them from the lungs' natural defences long enough to cause problems for susceptible individuals. This work was later taken up at Napier University by Donaldson who demonstrated that the diffusible compound from the spores interfered at the very basic cellular level by releasing toxic oxygen free radicals, so giving this fungus a survival advantage.[18]

Synthetic vitreous fibres (SVF)

The recognition that such a useful fibre for industry as asbestos carried a high risk to human health focused attention on substitute fibres with insulative and reinforcing qualities. Previously known as glass fibres or man-made vitreous fibres, the synthetic vitreous and refractory fibres were obvious candidates and were already in use. However, their fibrous shape begged obvious questions as to their safety. A large-scale five-year study of the main classes of SVF began in IOM in the late 1980s, co-funded by the Colt Foundation and the vitreous fibres industries. The aim was to develop a structure-toxicity paradigm for these fibres and to develop short-term testing strategies. The programme included three large-scale inhalation studies and many short-term testing approaches. It delivered a firm outcome regarding a structure-toxicity paradigm for SVF, finding that it was the same as that for asbestos. SVF that were non-biopersistent dissolved and shortened in the lungs[19] and thin, long and biopersistent fibres were pathogenic.[20,21] The large majority of the common SVF used for home insulation – stonewool and slagwool fibres – were not biopersistent and thus unlikely to be hazardous. However, the issue of biopersistence created unique problems for the interpretation of *in vitro* and short-term assays. The duration of an *in vitro* assay is typically less than forty-eight hours and the conditions in the cell culture do not mimic the conditions a fibre encounters residing in the lungs, so no influence of biopersistence is exerted. Therefore, the short-term *in vitro* studies could not contribute much to elaborating the fibre paradigm. At the same time, working from a different theoretical direction, Dr (now Professor) Lang Tran, a highly creative mathematical modeller and computational toxicologist, developed a model describing the essential behaviour of non-biopersistent SVF in the lungs that quantified dissolution and breakage of vitreous fibres.[22]

Low-toxicity dusts and lung overload

By the late 1980s attention was being focused on particles generally thought to be harmless or of low toxicity when inhaled by humans, such as carbon, titanium dioxide (TiO_2) and diesel soot. Alarm bells had rung when studies showed that long-term inhalation by rats of airborne concentrations of these low-toxicity dusts, at around the levels to which they were regulated in workplaces, caused a sudden failure of dust clearance with a consequent rapid build-up of dust allied to the onset of inflammation; this concept was called 'rat lung overload'. Scarring of the lung and cancer then followed, a consequence of the inflammation. Tran examined the kinetics of accumulation of low-toxicity dust in rat lungs in relation to the onset of overload and developed a model that reflected the various compartments in the lungs. The model showed how particles moved between the compartments in the lead-up to overload, indicating that remarkable and sudden movement of the dust from the air spaces into the lung tissue occurred at the point of overload.[23]

Tran also focused on the structure-toxicity model for overload, and an important breakthrough occurred when he plotted the lung mass burden against the onset of the inflammatory response for two low-toxicity particles, barium sulphate and TiO_2. Although high lung burdens of either caused a sudden onset of overload, this occurred at entirely different mass thresholds. However, the barium sulphate particles were slightly larger than those of TiO_2; thus, a given mass of barium sulphate had a lower surface area than the same mass of TiO_2 particles. When the mass dose was recalculated as surface area dose and the surface area dose plotted against inflammation, the two curves collapsed into one, with a clear single surface area threshold for the onset of inflammation.[24] This was the first published description of the actual surface area dose representing the threshold for the onset of rat lung overload.

The issue of rat lung overload cast doubt on the use of rat studies to assess the risks from inhalation of low-toxicity dusts, and IOM continued its interest in the issue of regulation of such dusts.[25] In terms of the structure/toxicity paradigm for low toxicity particles, these studies clearly indicate that surface area represents the key structure that drives the overload-dependent inflammatory response in low-toxicity dusts. These overload studies sensitised IOM toxicologists to two obvious but critically important facts:

In an aerosol, for a given mass the number of particles increases as the diameter of the individual particles decreases; small particles have a cumulative higher surface area than the same mass of larger particles.

Thus, if toxicity of low-toxicity dusts depends on surface area as indicated by the above experiments, the size and number of particles are likely to be relevant to regulation and protection of those people exposed. The relevance of this will become apparent in the next section.

Air pollution particles and the origins of nanotoxicology

In Britain, the adverse health effects of air pollution came to public attention after the dense smog episodes in the winter of 1952, when many excess deaths had occurred from heart and lung diseases. Since then, pollution concentrations in UK cities had progressively been reduced and a general complacency set in until, in the early 1970s, studies in the USA started to show that harmful effects were still detectable at the much lower concentrations then pertaining. A network of monitoring stations was set up across the UK and the main material collected by these was of particles less than 10µm in diameter, primarily carbon (a traditionally low-toxicity dust). This, called PM_{10}, was weighed by a microbalance in sampling sites distributed across the country.[26]

In 1994 Donaldson arranged to obtain PM_{10} from the filters at a sampling site in central Edinburgh to use in rat instillation and *in vitro* studies. As regards the structure/toxicity paradigm for PM_{10}, its ability to generate potentially inflammatory free radicals via transition metals was demonstrated by Dr Peter Gilmour,[27] and Dr Yang Li showed that the free radicals from PM_{10} were capable of causing oxidative stress and thereby initiating lung inflammation.[28] This latter study, the first on the toxicology of PM_{10} in the UK, initiated a large body of research into the cellular and molecular effects of urban air pollutants. The identification of transition metals as an important structural feature of PM_{10} that drove inflammation was subsequently confirmed in other laboratories and the oxidative potential of particles became an important part of the structure/ toxicity paradigm for many dusts, even being suggested as a metric for measuring PM and some other particles.[29,30]

In parallel with this research directed to the lung response, Seaton, then Professor of Environmental and Occupational Medicine in Aberdeen and an honorary member of IOM, had pointed out that the greater number of deaths associated with air pollution were from heart attack rather than lung disease. With Donaldson and colleagues from Edinburgh and Aberdeen universities, he published in *The Lancet* a hypothetical explanation, relating to the very small size of most air pollution particles, inflammation and blood clotting, proposing that the lung reacts to the number rather than the mass of inhaled particles, responding as though they were bacteria. This idea strongly influenced the future direction of the research worldwide.[31] Since particle toxicologists had thereto only been concerned with pulmonary effects and had no expertise in cardiovascular toxicology, this required scientists to refocus on solving the mystery of how particles depositing in the lungs caused adverse effects in the cardiovascular system.

Donaldson, then Professor of Respiratory Toxicology at the University of Edinburgh and an honorary member of IOM, was developing links with cardiologists. In collaboration with colleagues across Europe, human volunteers were exposed to ambient PM_{10} and diesel soot. They were able to show activation of multiple biological events leading to pro-thrombotic effects in the cardiovascular system following exposure. This work led to publications in the *New England Journal of Medicine and Circulation*, showing a mechanism whereby inhaling PM_{10} could increase the risk of heart attack and stroke, a world-leading advance.[32]

Manufactured nanoparticles

By the early 2000s recognition was growing that a new class of particles less than 100nm (nanoparticles, a nanometer being 1,000 millionth of a meter or 1,000th of a micrometer) was being manufactured and used by industry at an increasing and potentially alarming rate. Initially almost nothing was known about possible harmfulness of such particles to man and the environment, but the understanding of surface area as a driver of inflammation gained from the experiments described above, and the particles' high surface area relative to mass suggested the possibility of toxicity. In 2004, in response to expressed anxieties about such possible hazards of nanoparticles being used widely in industry, the UK Government commissioned a report from the Royal Society and the Royal Academy of Engineering on the opportunities and risks presented by new nanotechnologies.[33] In particular, Seaton, as a member of the committee, pointed to the knowledge gained from the asbestos experiments described above and the concept that cardiac risks of air pollution related to very small (described as ultrafine at the time) particles were responsible for the cardiac effects. The report highlighted carbon nanotubes and the general issue of nanofibers, a new type of fibre introduced into a workforce that might not be prepared to prevent possible risks, recalling the asbestos experience. It also drew attention to the possible hazard from inhalation or skin absorption of large numbers of very small particles. That year, an editorial described a new science of nanotoxicology and its scope, although no one then could have imagined the scientific impact it was to have.[34] Subsequently, the Colt Foundation funded Donaldson's group for a study on the similarities between asbestos and nanotubes in the light of the fibre paradigm. This led to a new research collaboration between IOM, Edinburgh, Aberdeen and Heriot Watt universities, as described in chapter 9. A 2009 paper in *Nature* arising from this research, led by Dr Craig Poland, reported that carbon nanotubes adhered to the fibre paradigm of length,[35] and later papers showed that carbon nanotubes were biopersistent and therefore fully satisfied the criteria for pathogenic fibres.

Chapter 7: References and Notes

1. This is discussed in Seaton A. (2018). *Farewell, King Coal: From industrial triumph to climatic disaster.* Dunedin Academic: Edinburgh.

2. Davis JMG, Chapman J, Collings P, Douglas AN, Fernie J, Lamb D, Ruckley VA. (1983). Variations in the histological patterns of the lesions of coal workers' pneumoconiosis in Britain and their relationship to lung dust content. *American Review of Respiratory Disease*; 128: 118-124.

3. Ruckley VA, Fernie JM, Chapman J, Collings P, Davis JMG, Douglas AN, Lamb D, Seaton A. (1984). Comparison of radiographic appearances with associated pathology and lung dust content in a group of coalworkers. *British Journal of Industrial Medicine*; 41: 459-467.

4. Douglas AN, Robertson A, Chapman JS, Ruckley VA. (1986). Dust exposure, dust recovered from the lung, and associated pathology in a group of British coalminers. *British Journal of Industrial Medicine*; 43: 795-901.

5. Ruckley VA, Gauld SJ, Chapman J, Davis JMG, Douglas AN, Fernie JM, Jacobsen M, Lamb D. (1984). Emphysema and dust exposure in a group of coal workers. *American Review of Respiratory Disease*; 129: 528-532.

6. The letters p and q (and r) refer to different average sizes of the small radiological opacities recorded in the ILO classification, as detailed in chapter 5. Fernie JM, Ruckley VA. (1978). Coalworkers' pneumoconiosis: correlation between opacity profusion and number and type of dust lesions, with special reference to opacity type. *British Journal of Industrial Medicine*; 44: 273-277.

7. In order to reach the outer linings of the lung or intestine (the pleura or peritoneum) inhaled fibres must traverse the

lung. Different types of asbestos were ultimately found to do this with differing degrees of efficiency, so a shortcut was to inject the fibres directly into the tissue. See Bolton RE, Davis JM, Donaldson K, Wright A. (1982). Variations in the carcinogenicity of mineral fibres. *Annals of Occupational Hygiene*; 26: 569-582.

8. Davis JM, Addison J, Bolton RE, Donaldson K, Jones AD, Smith T. (1986). The pathogenicity of long versus short fibre samples of amosite asbestos administered to rats by inhalation and intraperitoneal injection. *British Journal of Experimental Pathology*; 67: 415-430.

9. Davis JM, Jones AD. (1988). Comparisons of the pathogenicity of long and short fibres of chrysotile asbestos in rats. *British Journal of Experimental Pathology*; 69: 717-737.

10. Davis JM. (1989). Mineral fibre carcinogenesis: experimental data relating to the importance of fibre type, size, deposition, dissolution and migration. *IARC Scientific Publications*; 90: 33-45.

11. Gormley IP, Collings P, Davis JM, Ottery J. (1979). An investigation into the cytotoxicity of respirable dusts from British collieries. *British Journal of Experimental Pathology*; 60: 526-536.

12. It was and is standard practice when examining the toxicity of a dust to compare it with that of dusts of contrasting known severe and very low toxicity.

13. Donaldson K, Brown GM, Brown DM, Robertson MD, Slight J, Cowie H, Jones AD, Bolton RE, Davis JMG. (1990). Contrasting bronchoalveolar leukocyte responses in rats inhaling coal mine dust, quartz, or titanium dioxide: effects of coal rank, airborne mass concentration, and cessation of exposure. *Environmental Research*; 52: 62-76.

14. Donaldson K, Tran CL. (2002). Inflammation caused by particles and fibers. *Inhalation Toxicology*; 4: 5-27.

15. Brown GM, Donaldson K. (1989). Inflammatory responses in lungs of rats inhaling coal-mine dust – enhanced proteolysis

of fibronectin by bronchoalveolar leukocytes. *British Journal of Industrial Medicine*; 46: 866-872.

16. Robertson MD, Seaton A, Raeburn JA, Milne LJ. (1987). Inhibition of phagocyte migration and spreading by spore diffusates of *Aspergillus fumigatus*. *Journal of Medical and Veterinary Mycology*; 25: 389-396.

17. Seaton A, Robertson MD. (1989). Aspergillus, asthma, and amoebae. *Lancet*; 1: 893-894.

18. Slight J, Nicholson WJ, Mitchell CG, Pouilly N, Beswick PH, Seaton A, Donaldson K. (1996). Inhibition of the alveolar macrophage oxidative burst by a diffusible component from the surface of the spores of the fungus *Aspergillus fumigatus*. *Thorax* ; 51: 389-396.

19. Searl A, Buchanan D, Cullen RT, Jones AD, Miller BG, Soutar CA. (1999). Biopersistence and durability of nine mineral fibre types in rat lungs over 12 months. *Annals of Occupational Hygiene*; 43: 155-166.

20. Miller BG, Jones AD, Searl A, Buchanan D, Cullen RT, Soutar CA, Davis JM, Donaldson K. (1999). Influence of characteristics of inhaled fibres on development of tumours in the rat lung. *Annals of Occupational Hygiene*; 43: 167-179.

21. Miller BG, Searl A, Davis JM, Donaldson K, Cullen RT, Bolton RE, Buchanan D, Soutar CA. (1999). Influence of fibre length, dissolution and biopersistence on the production of mesothelioma in the rat peritoneal cavity. *Annals of Occupational Hygiene*; 43: 155-166.

22. Tran CL, Jones AD, Miller BG, Donaldson K. (2003). Modelling the retention and clearance of man-made vitreous fibers in the rat lung. *Inhalation Toxicology*; 15: 553-587.

23. Tran CL, Jones AD, Cullen RT, Donaldson K. (1999). Exploration of the mechanisms of retention and clearance of low-toxicity particles in the rat lung using a mathematical model. *Inhalation Toxicology*; 11: 403-409.

24. Tran CL, Buchanan D, Cullen RT, Searl A, Jones AD, Donaldson K. (2000). Inhalation of poorly soluble particles. II. Influence of particle surface area on inflammation and clearance. *Inhalation Toxicology*; 12: 1113-1126.

25. Cherrie JW, Brosseau LM, Hay A, Donaldson K. (2013), Low-toxicity dusts: current exposure guidelines are not sufficiently protective. *Annals of Occupational Hygiene*; 57: 685-691.

26. See chapter 6 for discussion of air sampling. PM denotes Particulate Matter and the subscript indicates the approximate aerosol diameter of the particles in micrometers (millionths of a meter) above which larger particles are excluded by the instrument's orifice. Usual metrics recorded for air pollution studies are particles less than 10 and 2.5μm in aerosol diameter.

27. This and the following studies were important in showing that a critical factor in making small combustion particles toxic is likely to be the presence of substances such as metallic ions (for example of iron) and complex chemical substances such as polycyclic aromatic hydrocarbons on the surface of the particle. These substances can initiate an inflammatory reaction by release of free oxygen radicals. Gilmour PS, Brown DM, Lindsay TG, Beswick PH, MacNee W, Donaldson K. (1996). Adverse health-effects of PM_{10} particles – involvement of iron in generation of hydroxyl radical. *Occupational and Environmental Medicine*; 53: 817-822.

28. Li XY, Gilmour PS, Donaldson K, MacNee, W. (1996). Free radical activity and pro-inflammatory effects of particulate air pollution (PM_{10}) *in vivo* and *in vitro*. *Thorax*; 51: 1216-1222.

29. Donaldson K, Beswick PH, Gilmour PS. (1996). Free radical activity associated with the surface of particles: a unifying factor in determining biological activity? *Toxicology Letters*; 88: 293-298.

30. Ayres JG, Borm P, Cassee FR, Castranova V, Donaldson K, Ghio A, Harrison RM, Hider R, Kelly F, Kooter IM, Marano F,

Maynard RL, Mudway I, Nel A, Sioutas C, Smith S, Baeza-Squiban A, Cho A, Duggan S, Froines J. (2008). Evaluating the toxicity of airborne particulate matter and nanoparticles by measuring oxidative stress potential – a workshop report and consensus statement. *Inhalation Toxicology*; 20: 75-99.

31. The original hypothesis proposed that the lung reacts to inhaled particles as though they were bacteria, causing an inflammatory reaction that increases blood coagulability, thus increasing the risks in individuals of obstruction of the coronary arteries to the heart. This explained why such very small masses of carbon particles could cause heart attack when inhaled into the lungs. Seaton A, MacNee W, Donaldson K, Godden D. (1995). Particulate air pollution and acute health effects. *Lancet*; 345: 176-178.

32. Wilson SJ, Miller MR, Newby DE. (2018). Effects of diesel exhaust on cardiovascular function and oxidative stress. *Antioxidants and Redox Signaling*; 28: 819-836.

33. Royal Society and Royal Academy of Engineering. (2004). Nanoscience and nanotechnologies: opportunities and uncertainties. London: The Royal Society.

34. Donaldson K, Stone V, Tran CL, Kreyling W, Borm PJA. (2004). Nanotoxicology: a new frontier in particle toxicology relevant to both the workplace and general environment and to consumer safety. *Occupational and Environmental Medicine*; 61: 727-728.

35. Poland CA, Duffin R, Kinloch I, Maynard A, Wallace WAH, Seaton A, Stone V, Brown S, MacNee W, Donaldson K. (2008). Carbon nanotubes introduced into the abdominal cavity of mice show asbestos-like pathogenicity in a pilot study. *Nature Nanotechnology*; 3: 423-428.

8

Ergonomics at IOM

Summary

IOM has been a significant contributor for decades to what is still a relatively young discipline. The UK Ergonomics Research Society (the oldest such society worldwide, and now the Chartered Institute of Ergonomics and Human Factors) is only ten years older than ergonomics at IOM itself. As well as supporting the work of that Society (providing a President, an Honorary General Secretary, a Treasurer as well as several members of council and other contributors), IOM has developed a leading role through its research work, in the UK, Europe and the wider world. Under the successive leadership of Tom Leamon, Geoff Simpson and Dr Richard Graveling, many IOM ergonomists have established international reputations – a position that continues to this day – providing an authoritative and independent voice to the UK Government and the EU, as well as to industry bodies, trade unions and others.

From their early years in coal mining research, through IOM's transition to an independent organisation with multiple sources of funding, IOM ergonomists have maintained important roles in key areas of work such as musculoskeletal disorders and psychological stress, both still extremely relevant today as the major causes of work-related sickness absence. Other studies have embraced protection from heat and noise, safe design of machines and workplaces, and safe handling of materials. As times and the workplace have changed, additional challenges have appeared, and IOM researchers have been quick to recognise this and again develop important roles. Under the latest leadership of Dr Joanne Crawford, issues relating to ageing workers (a demographic shift of concern worldwide) and the broader application of 'safe and healthy work at any age', are now being addressed.

The early years

Ergonomics featured in the work of IOM from its inception, starting on a relatively small scale with, for example, studies on the adverse effects of thin-seam working in UK coal mines by Dr Alan Knight and research on the fitness of mines rescue men by Ken Sweetland. Knight had started his career as an underground worker in the East Midlands coalfield before becoming an ergonomist and earning his PhD from Loughborough University. In contrast, Sweetland had been involved in academic research on coal mining issues prior to the founding of IOM, working with Professor Sandy Lind at Oxford University on issues such as heat stress, where Lind had been responsible for the development of the eponymous Lind Tables, used to establish safe working times for mines rescue men wearing self-contained breathing apparatus.

Expansion and success in winning European grants

More extensive studies in ergonomics at IOM began with the creation of an ergonomics branch in early 1976. Toward the end of 1975 the National Coal Board (NCB) had realised that there was significant funding available (from the European Coal and Steel Community – ECSC) to support ergonomics studies, which they had not previously tapped into. David Muir, then Head of Medical Branch at IOM, was asked to submit proposals to this funding stream, and he appointed Tom Leamon to head up the development of an ergonomics function based on joint NCB/ECSC funding. Leamon, in conjunction with Ian Drayton and Phil Ashby, prepared six submissions, on the assumption that only two might be accepted. To everyone's surprise all six were funded. When this surprise outcome was raised, the NCB, rather than choosing to undertake two or three, asked the Institute to accept all six. This meant that the four people in post at that time would need to increase to almost thirty in order to fulfil the commitments.

In late 1976, Geoff Simpson was appointed deputy to Tom Leamon and, as his first task, was given the recruitment of a large team of ergonomics specialists, thereby creating the IOM ergonomics branch. It soon became apparent that there would not be sufficient room at the Institute's Edinburgh home and, as a result, it was decided that the ergonomics branch would be based on the site of the Mining Research and Development Establishment (MRDE) at Bretby, near Burton-on-Trent in the English Midlands. Within six months the branch had grown from five to thirty-two (twenty-eight graduate researchers, three technicians and a secretary). It was decided to create two subgroups within the branch, one dealing with man-machine systems (headed by Steve Mason) and one with environmental issues (headed by Rod Graves). Dr Richard Graveling joined two years later (1978) to head up a group dealing with aspects of work physiology and biomechanics.

The first six projects undertaken covered a wide variety of topics encompassing many different aspects of mining activities including the effects of underground thermal environments; the ergonomics of underground haulage and transport operations;[1] and the task of the operator in a colliery control room. As an interesting aside, the most severe climates encountered in UK coal mines at the time were similar to those met on a daily basis by the inhabitants of Singapore (without the sunshine). As an illustration of the difficulties encountered in carrying out practical research in underground environments, a study of the physical loads and demands on coalface workers required equipment designed to record heart rate to be especially adapted and certified as 'intrinsically safe', that is unable to spark off an explosion or fire, before it could be used underground. Towards the end of the first round of ECSC projects, Tom Leamon left to take up an academic appointment in the USA and Geoff Simpson was promoted to Head of Branch.

A second round of ECSC/NCB-funded projects covered an equally diverse range of topics and aspects of coal mining operations including: communications in noisy environments;[2] the design of underground development machines; underground illumination;[3] and a study of accident prevention measures in work in coal bunkers. Following an NCB report that identified that more man shifts were devoted to maintenance than to coal production, one study looked at ergonomic aspects of the maintenance of mining machinery. Maintaining large items of equipment in the harsh underground environment was particularly challenging. Space constraints could make even the simplest task difficult and, for any major work, machinery would have to be dismantled and taken to the surface before it could be repaired. As a result of this work, ergonomics design guidelines were prepared so that future equipment would be better designed for (relative) ease of maintenance. This project was one of those that resulted in IOM receiving the first of three awards from the Ergonomics Society (see below).

Coal mines frequently incorporated large vertical shafts spanning two or more seams that were used as buffer stores to smooth the flow of coal to the surface. These bunkers created particular concerns, because of the relatively high proportion of accidents that resulted in fatalities, to those who needed to go into them from time to time (usually for maintenance or repair). An ergonomics project explored many different facets of the work and possible contributory causes to this problem. This included the risk perception of the workforce; the design of access points; and the design of the fall-arrest harnesses and other devices that were used by those who entered them. This mixture of physical ergonomics and the more psychological human factor elements provides a good example of the breadth of skills offered by IOM staff.

Machine design and the Swadlincote Man

Aside from these major projects, one of the early successes of the ergonomics branch was to persuade the MRDE senior staff that ergonomics should be routinely included in the trials for approval of new mining equipment (undertaken at the surface test site close to MRDE in Swadlincote) before authorisation for use underground. It was during one of these trials that the now well-known 'Swadlincote Man' was discovered (a relative of Cranfield Man, who was designed to operate a particular type of lathe, a feature of ergonomics texts at the time). In the NCB's case, a new roadway development machine, known as a drill-loader, was being assessed. This machine was designed to advance the underground tunnels by drilling a shot-firing pattern and then, after the shots had been fired, it collected the debris and loaded it onto a conveyor belt to be carried back out of the tunnel [fig 8.1].

Fig 8.1: Mining machine (drill loader) indicating one of the positions the operator may need to adopt

The ergonomics assessment of this machine identified so many design limitations that it was apparent it would be easier to redesign the operator than the machine. The genetic engineering prototype for a new operator is shown below (designed by ergonomist Steve Mason), alongside his more normal companion [fig 8.2].

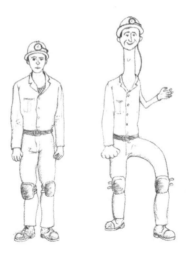

Fig 8.2: Swadlincote Man

The new operator incorporated the following design features:

- An elongated neck to see over the drill booms which were directly in the normal operator's line of sight
- A short left arm, more easily to reach a bank of twelve controls positioned very close to the normal operator's shoulder;
- A very large right hand to operate the two track controls (i.e. to turn the machine left the operator had to simultaneously push the left track lever forward and the right track lever backwards)
- Bow legs to avoid the eight control levers positioned between the knees
- A shortened right leg to comfortably reach the dead-man's pedal, which was positioned very close to the seat

Unfortunately, Swadlincote Man never found his way into production, but the illustration served well to illustrate the shortcomings of some machinery being provided for miners to operate underground.

Winning awards

In 1982, the ergonomics branch was awarded the Application of Ergonomics Award (now the Otto Edholm Award) by the then Ergonomics Society (now the Chartered Institute of Ergonomics and Human Factors – CIEHF). This was awarded for what became known as the 'Design Aids for Designers' approach.[4] Essentially this involved collating all the ergonomics guidelines relevant to a particular type of equipment into a single source. So, for example, an engineer designing an underground locomotive would only need the report entitled 'Ergonomics Principles for the Design of Underground Locomotives' rather than searching through generic ergonomics documents and trying to decide which were relevant to his current area of interest. As well as that for maintenance referred to earlier, 'Design Aids for Designers' reports produced by IOM encompassed underground locomotives, free-steered vehicles and roof bolting equipment.

The following year (1983), the branch was awarded the premier award of the (then) Ergonomics Society – the Sir Frederick Bartlett Medal [fig 8.3]. This award was given in recognition of the branch's contribution both to mining ergonomics[5] and to the wider ergonomics discipline[6,7].

Fig 8.3: The Sir Frederick Bartlett Medal

Other research
Communication in noise

During the remainder of the 1980s, most of the work of the branch continued to focus on ECSC-funded projects. Considerable work was done on communication in noisy environments (under Graham Coleman), including the development of a new approach to tailoring auditory warning signals to the ambient noise. This involved identifying the frequencies that would not be masked by frequencies within the ambient noise. Noise-related work also included a detailed approach to the selection of hearing defenders, dependent on both the ambient noise and any auditory warning signals used in a given area.

Manual handling

Two other areas of work involved a return to the early days of ergonomics in IOM – work physiology and biomechanics. This included an examination of the biomechanics of mine supplies handling using the intra-abdominal pressure technique (developed originally at the University of Surrey). This entailed volunteer mineworkers swallowing a pressure-sensitive 'pill' that transmitted a radio signal showing the pressure being exerted on it as it passed through the alimentary canal in the abdominal cavity.[8,9] Earlier work at the university had established this as a measure of the strain experienced when handling heavy loads.

This focus on the biomechanics of manual handling led the ECSC Committee of Experts to commission IOM to produce a guidance document on safe manual handling for application across the European mining industries. This was published by ECSC Community Ergonomics Action Programme (translated into all the relevant languages of ECSC) as 'Guidelines for Manual Handling in the Coal Industry' and subsequently referenced in the UK Health and Safety Executive's (HSE) Guidelines on manual handling as a model of industry-specific advice on safe manual handling. Around the same time, IOM compiled published objective weight limits for manual handling, providing material to support the development of guidance weight charts for the same guidelines. These remain part of the HSE guidelines to the present day and have been adopted by Ireland and other countries.

Heat stress underground

Following on from the early ECSC project on adverse thermal environments, a series of projects explored aspects of heat stress in underground working. With a strong input from Len Morris, one of IOM's ergonomists at the time, these included:

- fundamental research ('Response to intermittent work in hot environments') that contributed to collaborative ECSC work that was used in the development of a new International Standard on predicting the risk of heat stress;[10]
- a detailed examination of a wide range of published heat stress indices, including both a review of their theoretical justification and their practicality;
- more practically-orientated studies such as exploring the feasibility of using cooling garments for machine operators (using 'active man-cooling' technology pioneered in the aerospace industry);
- and a review of the risks and control measures ('Working in hot conditions in mining· a literature review') that was subsequently adopted by the HSE as a guidance document for the industry.

In a return to the work of IOM's predecessors, Graveling led a team that developed permissible wearing times for rescue personnel using a new self-contained breathing apparatus (the SEFA). This apparatus had been developed by the Mines Rescue Service as a replacement for the original Proto self-rescuer and new charts were needed to replace the earlier Lind Charts.

A new beginning: transition to the new IOM

The years leading up to the formation of the new IOM presented a quandary for the staff of the ergonomics branch. The staff had spent many years striving to establish the value of the ergonomics discipline to the coal mining industry, and now British Coal (BC, the successor to the NCB) wanted to establish a separate ergonomics function at MRDE. At the same time, recognising the wider value of ergonomics, IOM also wanted to retain an ergonomics function. As a result, when the Institute became independent of BC, the ergonomics branch split, with one group (under Graveling) continuing as part of IOM and moving to the Edinburgh HQ and a second group (under Simpson) staying in Staffordshire and transferring to become part of the Technical Services and Research Executive of BC.

Under the leadership of Graveling, the years spanning the transition to the new IOM saw the growth of work on musculoskeletal disorders and the emergence of HSE as a significant source of funding for ergonomics-related work (and a growth in the collaborative work between parts of the Institute that is a hallmark of much of its work). Some of this activity (e.g. studies of aspects of back pain in coal miners) continued to be funded by ECSC, while other work, such as the development of an early assessment tool for work-related upper limb disorders, epidemiological studies of such disorders amongst computer users,[11] and the evaluation of manual handling guidance,[12,13,14] were supported by HSE. As mentioned in an earlier chapter, this period even saw the short-term employment of a research midwife to support a study of lifting by pregnant women. However, the origins of IOM within coal mining (and the strand of work on heat stress) were not forgotten, with the commissioning by the new privatised coal mining companies of guidance on the management of heat stress.

Personal protective equipment

Firefighters

The ergonomics of personal protective equipment (PPE) had been an element of IOM's work for many years, including that on hearing defenders referred to earlier, and studies of fall-arrest harnesses[15] and of respiratory protection.[16,17,18] Fittingly, in the year of the fortieth anniversary of the foundation of IOM, this element of IOM's work was recognised by CIEHF by the award of the President's Medal (now the President's Award), making this the third CIEHF award earned by IOM since its inception.

Part of the research that earned that honour combined the two strands of heat stress and the ergonomics of PPE in the workplace (funded by the Home Office). Initially under the leadership of Richard Love, a physiologist who had been responsible for early work on acceptable levels of breathing resistance for respiratory protection, this involved studies of firefighters' clothing,[19] self-contained breathing apparatus (including the then new lightweight fibre-wrapped compressed air cylinders) and fire hoods. Up until that time there had been some resistance within the UK fire service to the use of fire hoods, with the belief that firefighters needed to have some skin exposed to provide a safeguard ("when your ears start burning you know it is time to get out"), as well as the idea that exposed ears were essential for directional sound location. This IOM research helped to change such attitudes and beliefs, and the modern firefighter now routinely wears such hoods as an essential part of their protective ensemble.

Studies on firefighters became a significant strand of research in later years, with IOM ergonomists (under Graveling), collaborating with other researchers (e.g. Optimal Performance Ltd) to explore other elements of the work of firefighters, especially in a series of projects prompted by the tragic events in New York now simply known as '9/11'. Again, reflecting another circle in the activities of IOM, this latter work included the use of a swallowed sensor, in this case one that measured and transmitted body temperature as it passed through the body.

London Underground

One interesting development saw the expansion of the research on heat stress outside the workplace – to the London Underground. As part of a major initiative to improve ventilation and reduce temperatures in the underground network ('Cooling the Tube'), preliminary desk-top research was followed by collaborative research between IOM, Qinetiq and Optimal Performance. In this study, the IOM workshop designed and built a mock-up of part of the interior of an underground train carriage. This was then dismantled and transported to a climate chamber at Qinetiq, where it was reassembled and populated by volunteer members of the public in a series of experiments. This research provided objective data on what could happen (both to the carriage climate and the passengers) when a crowded train lost power, stranding passengers in a warm underground tunnel. The mock-up incorporated an air recirculation system that could simulate the back-up ventilation system built in to the carriages. The results were used to refine and validate predictive models developed to help London Underground prioritise those areas of the underground network most in need of cooling solutions. Figure 8.4a shows the outside of the mock-up, assembled in a climate chamber and the inside showing the London Underground seats and dividers included into the design [fig 8.4b].

Fig 8.4: Outside (a) and inside (b) view of a mock
London Underground train, built by IOM.

Collaborations in Europe: IOM's influence

Other chapters in this book point to the importance of European funding in supporting the research of IOM. Ergonomics (now called the Ergonomics and Human Factors section, under the leadership of Joanne Crawford) is no exception to this. IOM ergonomists have benefited from research funded both by the European Commission and the European Union Information Agency for Occupational Safety and Health (EU OSHA). Two projects serve to illustrate the breadth of this work (again demonstrating collaborative working, both across IOM and with other researchers). The first, funded by the Commission, was a major collaborative venture that entailed the evaluation of the impact of all twenty-four of the EU occupational safety and health directives that form the basis of health and safety legislation in every Member State. Under the lead of Graveling, IOM researchers were responsible for the preparation of individual reports on twelve of these (including of course those relating to ergonomics) with recommendations for their retention, revision or (in one case) repeal, as well as being part of the core team for the overall review.[20]

In a second (and very different) piece of work, this time funded by the European Agency for Safety and Health at Work (EU OSHA), IOM ergonomics and human factors staff prepared the text for an e-guide on 'psychosocial risks' (stress), subsequently overseeing its translation into thirty-three different versions reflecting different languages and legal provisions. This represented the most recent activity in a field of research that again has its origins in the coal mining years (stress amongst coal mine managers) and led to work, funded by the Health Education Board for Scotland, that developed an early stress risk assessment tool.

Health and safety in a changing world

The changing age demographic of the workplace has also been examined by IOM researchers in trying to gain a better understanding of the impact of age on work and work on ageing.[21,22] As an illustration of the independence of IOM and the broad reach of its client base, this research included a review of ageing and firefighters on behalf of the Fire Brigades Union. This important area of work, developed by Crawford, has also included systematic reviews for the Institute of Occupational Safety and Health (IOSH) to examine the health, safety and health promotion needs of older workers.[23] This work was followed by the Safer and Healthier at Any Age project, funded by EU OSHA. Within this project a broader understanding of the occupational health needs across the European Union was identified for older workers as well as a state-of-the-art review into women and the ageing workforce and their occupational health needs. This work encompassed reviews and case studies which are now available from EU OSHA across all twenty-eight EU countries. IOM staff also had input into the design of the e-guide 'Safety and Health at All Ages'. Given the projections for an ageing workforce worldwide, it is likely that issues relating to the significance of such changes will continue to develop as a theme for IOM work in the future as will exploring the impact of different ways of working.[24]

Return to work and rehabilitation has also been a research topic, specifically the safety and health needs of people returning to or remaining in work after cancer diagnosis and treatment. This work, sponsored by IOSH, took a case study approach by engaging with individuals and companies who had successfully returned an individual to work to identify good practice. Guidance was developed as part of this project which is freely available on the IOSH website.

The ergonomics and human factors section also took part in the first of IOSH's research programmes where five projects were funded under the banner of 'Health and Safety in a Changing World'. IOM led the project on knowledge management that examined the occupational safety and health landscape in the UK and how professionals and those tasked with safety roles use safety and health knowledge to intervene in the workplace. The project reviewed the knowledge base in the UK and then carried out twelve case studies with a mixture of small, medium and large organisations who had or were about to implement change; four of the case studies were prospective. The framework for this work was the 'Diffusion of Innovations Theory', intended to help understand how information and knowledge can be designed for easier transfer in different working environments.

IOM's long history of work in relation to musculoskeletal disorders[25,26] has continued in its relationship with EU OSHA. The next campaign for EU OSHA will be on musculoskeletal disorders and IOM continues with them to look at preventive measures and the management of chronic musculoskeletal problems. This represents the fourth campaign in a row where work by IOM researchers has provided support material.

Extending the reach of the Institute's ergonomics work

Building on the successful development of IOM Singapore, described in chapter 4, ergonomics and human factors staff, supported by others from the Research Division, obtained funding for an important new piece of work from that country's Workplace Safety and Health Institute. Under the leadership of Graveling this study merges two long-standing areas of research (musculoskeletal disorders[27] and stress[28,29]) to address increasing concerns about the use of devices such as smartphones. Parallel strands of the study have explored epidemiological aspects of the use of such devices and possible muscular disorders, while also examining aspects of the 'always on' culture – and its possible effect on work-life balance.

Ergonomics and IOM Consulting Ltd

One feature of the work of IOM ergonomists over the years, increasing in scale in the 'new' IOM, is that, as well as their research activities, staff also provide consultancy services, making their expertise available to industry groups, employers and unions covering a wide range of topics and industries. Much of this work mirrors the research strands described above with consultancy work relating to heat stress, musculoskeletal disorders and psychological stress amongst others. This has seen IOM ergonomists working for individual fire brigades, on offshore oil installations, in nuclear and coal-fired power stations, and of course, being based in Scotland, the salmon and whisky-producing industries to name a few. Some of this work has been published as research while other work, carried out through IOM Consulting Ltd, has provided confidential advice and guidance to clients, underpinned by the research knowledge acquired over the years. Over the last few years, IOM ergonomists have also provided support to consultants in IOM Singapore, offering ergonomics and stress-related services and helping them to develop a wider range of services in the Far East. There are clearly many opportunities for further future development of these services in a changing world of work.

Chapter 8: References and Notes

1. Sims MT, Graves RJ, Simpson GC. (1983). Mineworkers' scores on the Group Embedded Figures Test. *Journal of Occupational Psychology*; 56: 335-337.

2. Simpson GC, Coleman GJ. (1988). The development of a procedure to ensure effective auditory warning signals. *Mining Engineer*; 147: 511-514.

3. Martin R, Graveling RA. (1983). Background illumination and its effects on peripheral awareness for miners using cap lamps. *Applied Ergonomics*; 14: 139-141.

4. Simpson GC, Mason S. (1983). Design aids for designers: an effective role for ergonomics. *Applied Ergonomics*; 14: 177-183.
5. Leamon TB. (1981). Ergonomics and improvements to working conditions in mines. *Mining Engineer*; 140: 473-476.
6. Simpson GC, Chan WL. (1988). The derivation of population stereotypes for mining machines and some reservations on the general applicability of published stereotypes. *Ergonomics*; 31: 327-335.
7. Simpson G. (1988). Promoting reliability: the human factor. *Mineral Resources Engineering*; 1: 3-11.
8. Graveling RA, Sims MT, Graves RJ. (1986). Intra-abdominal pressure responses of mineworkers to standard loads. *Applied Ergonomics*; 17: 105-109.
9. Sims M, Graveling RA. (1988). Manual handling of supplies in free and restricted headroom. *Applied Ergonomics*; 19: 289-292.
10. Graveling RA, Morris LA. (1995). Influence of intermittency and static components of work on heat stress. *Ergonomics*; 38: 101-114.
11. Melrose AS, Graveling RA, Cowie H, Ritchie P, Hutchison P, Mulholland RM. (2007). Better display screen equipment (DSE) work-related ill health data. Sudbury: HSE Books. (Research Report No. 561).
12. Tesh KM, Lancaster RJ, Hanson MA, Ritchie PJ, Donnan PT, Graveling RA. (1997). Evaluation of the manual handling operations regulations 1992 and guidance. Volumes 1 and 2. Sudbury: HSE Books. (Contract Research Report No. 152/1997).
13. Melrose AS, Graham MK, Graveling RA , George JPK, Cowie H, Hutchison PA, Mulholland RE. (2006). Assessing the effectiveness of the manual handling assessment chart (MAC) and supporting website. Sudbury: HSE Books. (Research Report No. 486).

14. Graveling RA, Melrose AS, Hanson MA. (2003). The principles of good manual handling: achieving a consensus. Sudbury: HSE Books. (Contract Research Report No. 097/2003).

15. Rushworth AM, Mason S. (1987). Aids to selecting fall-arrest harnesses: The ergonomic considerations. *Safety Practitioner*; 5: 22-27.

16. Graveling R, Sánchez Jiménez A, Lewis C, Groat S. (2011). Protecting respiratory health: what should be the constituents of an effective RPE programme? *Annals of Occupational Hygiene*; 55: 230-238.

17. Hanson M. (1999). Development of a draft British Standard: the assessment of heat strain for workers wearing personal protective equipment. *Annals of Occupational Hygiene*; 43. 309-319.

18. Graveling RA. (2013). The ergonomics of personal protective equipment. Safety Management; April: 24-26.

19. Graveling RA, Johnstone JBG, Butler DM, Crawford J, Love RG, Maclaren WM, Ritchie P. (1999). Study of the degree of protection afforded by firefighters' clothing. London: Home Office Fire Research and Development Group. (Research Report Number 1/99).

20. European Commission. (2015). Evaluation of the practical implementation of the Occupational Safety and Health (OSH) directives in EU Member States. Main report. Brussels: European Commission. DG Employment, Social Affairs and Inclusion.

21. Wainwright D, Crawford J, Loretto W, Phillipson C, Robinson M, Shepherd S, Vickerstaff S, Weyman A. (2018). Extending working life and the management of change. Is the workplace ready for the ageing worker? *Ageing and Society*. 1-23.

22. Crawford JO. (2016). Older workers: workplace health evidence-based practice? [editorial]. *Occupational Medicine*; 66: 424-425.

23. Crawford JO, Graveling RA, Cowie HA, Dixon K. (2010). The health safety and health promotion needs of older workers. *Occupational Medicine*; 60: 184-192.

24. Crawford JO, MacCalman L, Jackson CA. (2011). The health and well-being of remote and mobile workers. *Occupational Medicine*; 61: 385-394.

25. Nazari J, Pope MH, Graveling RA. (2015). Feasibility of magnetic resonance imaging (MRI) in obtaining nucleus pulposus (NP) water content with changing postures. *Magnetic Resonance Imaging*; 33: 459-464.

26. Graveling R. (2018). *Ergonomics and Musculoskeletal Disorders (MSDs) in the Workplace: A Forensic and Epidemiological Analysis*. Boca Raton, Florida: CRC Press.

27. Graveling RA. (1991). The prevention of back pain from manual handling. *Annals of Occupational Hygiene*; 35: 427-432.

28. Lancaster RJ, Burtney E. (1999). Stress in the workplace: a risk assessment approach to reduction of risk. *International Journal of Mental Health Promotion*; 1: 15-20.

29. Lancaster RJ, Butler MP, Pilkington A. (1998). Workplace stress: an organisational approach. *The Mental Health Review*; 3: 16-20.

9

Nanotechnology risk: a new approach

Summary

Rapid scientific advances in the late 20th century led to the development of many new and potentially disruptive technologies and materials, providing new challenges to understanding both opportunities and risks to workers and the environment. One of the most prominent was nanotechnology which exploited the novel properties of materials at the nanoscale. IOM, with its background in particle toxicology and risk assessment, was well placed to address some of these challenges, particularly in relation to protection of those who might potentially be exposed to these new materials. Its work, with collaborators, had already shown that particle toxicity increased with surface area and had defined the physical properties that make fibrous particles toxic. Building on this background, IOM embarked on a strategy to develop nanotechnology risk as a scientific and business opportunity seeking to understand and explain risks and how they could be reduced. Taking advantage of UK Government and EU Framework Programmes, a broad collaborative research initiative with universities and institutes throughout Europe was built up, leading to fundamental changes in IOM's research strategy, by acting with enterprises to foresee and prevent problems associated with new technology. The success of this venture led also to the opening of a branch of IOM in Singapore. The proactive approach

IOM took demonstrated it was possible to raise the profile of a whole area of science, build capacity and credibility, and move the international agenda. It enabled IOM to develop in innovative ways, from new ideas about science communication to thinking in a new paradigm about risk research being key to supporting innovation.

A new science and new opportunities

At the end of the 20th century an extraordinary idea was taking shape. It was that the physical and chemical properties of a group of materials were dependent not just on their chemical composition but also on their size, and that these properties alter as the size becomes critically small. The science behind this idea has come to be known as nanoscience and its application as nanotechnology. These ideas were attributed to the thoughts and conjectures of Richard Feynman, an American theoretical physicist who won the Nobel Prize in 1965 and to whom the phrase *"there is plenty of room at the bottom"* is credited. Feynman described a process by which scientists would be able to manipulate individual atoms and molecules to create new materials with very different properties and applications. Although several definitions have subsequently been developed, nanotechnologies and the nanoscale are generally considered to be based on the use of materials in the size range of 1 to 100 nm, that is up to about 100,000 millionth of a meter. This is a range that also includes many large biological molecules as well as viruses and some bacteria. Nanoscale particles are not new in nature or in science, but the development of new instruments enabled scientists to better understand and take advantage of phenomena that occur at this scale. These phenomena are based on so-called 'quantum' effects which are observed when the size of particle is small compared to the wavelengths of the electrons in the atoms which comprise it. This can lead to remarkable changes in properties of a material such as its melting point, fluorescence, electrical conductivity and magnetic permeability, as a function of particle size. Of great interest also was that this was the same size range as many molecules involved in biological and cellular processes leading to speculation on possible new interactions between nanoparticles and biological systems.

The optimism concerning these new possibilities led to major new investment by governments and industries around the world. In the United States, President Clinton identified nanotechnology development as a national research priority. In 2000 the US National Nanotechnology Initiative (NNI) was launched: a Federal Government programme for science, engineering and technology research and development for nanoscale projects, with an envisaged annual budget in excess of $1 billion. The stated aims were to advance a world-class nanotechnology research and development (R&D) programme; foster the transfer of new technologies into products for commercial and public benefit; develop and sustain educational resources, a skilled workforce, and the supporting infrastructure and tools to advance nanotechnology; and support responsible development of nanotechnology. The NNI became a model for investment in other regions around the globe.

The European Community launched its own scientific research initiative, the Sixth Framework Programme (FP6) in 2002. Nanotechnologies and Nanoscience was one of seven thematic areas with an indicative budget of €1.3 billion (out of a total framework budget of €16 billion).[1] And in the UK, The Department of Trade and Industry (DTI) committed funding through the Technology Strategy Board (TSB) to encourage UK science and industry to exploit this new technology. In 2003 TSB launched the Micro and Nanotechnology (MNT) programme with funding which eventually rose to more than £150 million with the aim of establishing a number of 'open access facilities' for use by industry and others.

Concerns: new technologies, hazard and risk

Hazard in relation to a material or a process defines the possibility of harm occurring, whether from its production, use or disposal. It is a theoretical concept, based on understanding of the material's physical, chemical and biological properties and of its likely applications across the duration of its life. A hazardous material is one that could at some stage in its existence cause harm to organisms or the environment. In distinction, *risk* is a quantification of the likelihood of such harm occurring. Risk can only be assessed when the hazardous properties of the material or process and the methods of its use are understood. The hazardous properties of a material may be assessed by animal experiments (*in vivo*), by studies of cells and tissues in the laboratory (*in vitro*), or sometimes by computer-based computations (*in silico*).

New technologies are never without risk and the optimism and enthusiasm of scientists require to be balanced by a realistic assessment of any possible hazard from the production, use and ultimately disposal of the materials employed in the applications. A glance back at previous disruptive technologies is sufficient to justify this caution – use of fossil fuels, pharmaceuticals, plastics, and so on. All have brought benefits but later have caused huge unforeseen problems. Promotion of the predicted benefits of nanotechnologies was accompanied by voices of caution, including some from IOM. However, the first widely publicised warning was from an altogether more surprising source. In April 2003, HRH Prince Charles drew attention to potential risks from nanotechnology arising from a concept intriguingly titled the 'Grey Goo' theory. Grey Goo is a hypothetical end-of-the-world scenario involving molecular nanotechnology in which out-of-control self-replicating nano-robots consume all biomass on Earth to make copies of themselves. All life is exterminated and all that is left are piles of nano-robots. This was derived from science fiction, including the film *The Day the Earth Stood Still*. Although this seemed far-fetched, the graphic nature of this threat and the source of the information certainly had the effect of raising the issue in the public consciousness. In practice though, there were three areas of legitimate concern.

Particles become more toxic at very small size

As mentioned in chapter 7, in the late 1990s, IOM had run a programme of work investigating the toxicity of relatively inert dusts, such as titanium dioxide and barium sulphate, often referred to as 'low-toxicity dusts'. The purpose of this work, a step forward from studying coal mine dusts, was to try to understand the risks of particulate air pollution. One of the key findings was a correlation between the total surface area of the exposure dose and the lung inflammation, an index of toxicity.[2] By using surface area as a metric, the toxicity profile of dusts of different chemical composition could be collapsed onto a single line. From an understanding of geometry, the surface area of a simple (spherical) particle increases proportionately to the square of the radius. Thus, 1 mg of 10 nm particles would have the same surface area as 100 mg of 100 nm particles, a hundred-fold increase. The implications of this were that new materials with smaller particle size would in all probability be much more toxic than the same mass of the same material at a larger particle size, and that particles previously considered inert at larger sizes might become toxic at the nanoscale. This concept had already been demonstrated experimentally by the work of Prof Gunther Oberdörster and his colleagues in Albany in USA.

Inhaled small particles may cause effects on the heart and other organs

This is the second issue related to work on air pollution. Epidemiological studies had consistently shown an association between particulate air pollution and exacerbations of illness in people with respiratory disease and rises in the numbers of deaths from cardiovascular and respiratory disease among older people. In a publication in *The*

Lancet in 1995, Professor Anthony Seaton and Dr Ken Donaldson and their co-workers had hypothesised that the ultra-fine (nano) particles in air pollution are able to provoke alveolar inflammation, with release of mediators capable, in susceptible individuals, of causing exacerbations of lung disease and of increasing blood coagulability. This hypothesis, which suggested that the lung reacted to these nanoparticles as though they were invading micro-organisms provided an explanation for the observed increases in cardiovascular deaths associated with urban pollution episodes[3] [fig 9.1].

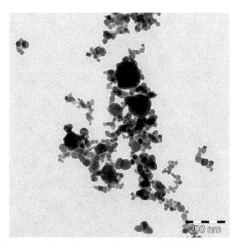

Fig 9.1: Transmission Electron Microscopy (TEM) image of copper oxide nanoparticles (Courtesy of Dr Matt Boyles, IOM)

Nanoparticles of fibrous shape may act like asbestos

A third area of concern came from IOM's work on asbestos and related to carbon nanotubes (CNT). As discussed in chapter 7, two important determinants of the toxicity of asbestos are the length and the diameter of the fibres, long and very thin fibres being most toxic. The diameter of many asbestos fibres is in the nano range. Carbon nanotubes (CNTs) were one of the most remarkable new products of nanotechnology [fig 9.2]. They comprise carbon atoms arranged in a cylindrical nanostructure and have unusual properties, such as exceptional strength and conductivity, making

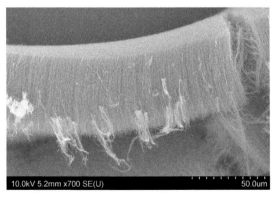

10.0kV 5.2mm x700 SE(U)   50.0um

Fig 9.2: Scanning Electron Microscopy (SEM) image of a mat of multiwall
carbon nanotubes (CNT) as they are collected immediately after manufacture.
Each individual nanotube is approximately 50 nm in diameter
and 50,000 nm in length (Courtesy of Dr Matt Boyles, IOM)

them valuable for electronics, optics and other fields of material
science and technology. Nanotubes had been synthesised with
diameters up to a few tens of *nano*meters, with lengths up to tens
or hundreds of *micro*meters. From a toxicological perspective,
however, CNTs could be thought of as durable (biopersistent)
high aspect ratio particles, directly analogous to asbestos fibres
with, in principle, the same potential for harm.

Perception of risk: IOM gets involved

In addition to these specific potential risks, an overriding concern
of the UK and other governments was public perception of the
risks. Some ten years earlier, another highly promising technology,
Genetically Modified Organisms (GMOs), fell foul of adverse public
comment and risk perception. The main application foreseen for this
technology was in the food sector, leading to media hyperbole and
fears about 'Frankenfoods'. Application of this technology stalled
because of these fears, and a major opportunity was lost. This led to
government and industry taking the view that a strategy to address
potential risks of nanotechnology was required. This would be the
first time that a new and disruptive technology was to be subjected

to a critical analysis of possible risks before any harm had actually occurred, an application of the precautionary principle.

In 2002, Dr Lang Tran, a creative and energetic computational toxicologist, who had led on parts of the low-toxicity dust programme (see chapter 7), and Dr Rob Aitken, then Director of Research Development and leader of IOM's Exposure Research Group (and who would subsequently become IOM's Chief Executive), had been discussing the emerging field of nanotechnology. Realising that the proposed huge financial investments would lead to greater use of (and therefore exposure of individuals and the environment to) potentially more toxic materials, they were considering how nanoparticle risk could be developed as both a scientific and business opportunity for IOM. IOM had demonstrable and relevant experience and expertise in the risks of fine particles though, by this time, little resource to investigate them. Tran and Aitken, working with Martie van Tongeren (then at the University of Birmingham, but who would subsequently join IOM), put together a programme for a workshop at a British Occupational Hygiene Society (BOHS) conference to bring together some of the key scientists in particle exposure and toxicology to highlight these issues and bring them to a wider audience. At the time, the terminology used was 'ultrafine particles' but the focus was on engineered (manufactured) nanoparticles. This was the first conference session in the UK to address specifically the health hazards associated with these materials. Some of the key questions identified at that workshop were:

- What is the best metric to measure exposure and harmfulness?
- Are people being exposed to manufactured nanoparticles or could they be exposed in the future?
- How can personal exposure be assessed?
- Have health effects been observed?
- How can exposure be controlled?
- What are safe exposure limits?

This conference was effective in clarifying some of the issues and questions and raising awareness. A seed had been planted.

Opportunities and uncertainties

In late 2003, at the request of the UK Government, the Royal Society and Royal Academy of Engineering set up a working group to review both the opportunities and uncertainties of nanoscience and its potential applications and risks. One of the members of the committee was Seaton who was instrumental in driving consideration of human health risks as part of the work of this committee. The output was a report, 'nanoscience and nanotechnologies: opportunities and uncertainties', published in 2004; it was the first significant publication to consider the key health risks and recommend actions to address them.[4] The report and the questions posed established a framework that would drive UK Government policy over the following decade. It also provided a call to action internationally to address these issues. A key message was that these risks should be addressed proactively, rather than waiting for the evidence of harm to present itself through mortality or morbidity in working populations or the wider public. Another important message was that the *toxicity* of these materials should not be considered in isolation. Rather, the potential for *exposure of individuals over the life course of the materials* should also be assessed so that a proper understanding of any risks could be developed.

The IOM strategy

It was beginning to become clear that government and industry were sufficiently concerned about the potential threats to adoption of multiple nanotechnologies from both perceived and real risks that they were considering investment to investigate and to manage them. Tran and Aitken embarked on a proactive approach to capitalise on the opportunity. The three main elements of the approach were: raising awareness of the issues through a series of high-profile publications, meetings with senior representatives in government, and invitations to talk at important meetings; working with others to build capacity and alliances in which partners brought complementary skills; and developing and implementing research programmes to answer the questions raised. These activities, carried out in parallel, defined the major part of IOM's work in this area for many years.

Raising awareness

Raising awareness presented some challenges. It was important that these issues were brought to the attention of industry, governments and other research funders. However, it was critical that issues were raised in a responsible manner so as not to generate undue fears and alarms. In short, a very measured but persistent approach was necessary. Tran and Aitken held a series of meetings with key government representatives in departments in the UK, notably those relating to trade, safety and the environment. In Europe, they met with Professor Renzo Tomellini, Head of the European Commission Nanotechnology Unit. One of the purposes of these meetings was to clarify the issues and find pathways to resolve them. A common feature of the meetings was that the representatives were focused only on the toxicity of nanoparticles. Inevitably, the question would be posed, *"but are nanoparticles toxic?"* In the early days a great deal of effort was necessary to encourage wider thinking about exposure and risk and about the possibility of different hazard groupings for different types (or classes) of nanoparticles. Tran and Aitken also accepted a series of speaking invitations and published many articles on the subject in relevant journals and commercial publications.

To bring further prominence to these issues, IOM worked with Dr Andrew Maynard, an accomplished scientist formerly with the Health and Safety Laboratory (HSL) in Buxton, who had moved to the Woodrow Wilson Institute, a think tank based in Washington DC. Maynard was an innovative science communicator, an early adopter of Twitter, and had established his own blogging site, 2020Science, with a strong focus on nanotechnology risk. Maynard proposed a high-profile publication in the journal Nature about nano-risk issues, and approached Aitken to develop a proposal to do that. The Woodrow Wilson Institute awarded a contract to IOM to do this work, and a writing workshop was held in IOM's Edinburgh office over two days in early 2006. The outcome was a paper published in *Nature* in 2006, only the second time that IOM had published in this prestigious journal, describing a series of grand challenges for nanotechnology risk [fig 9.3], with indicative timescales over which they should be achieved.[5] This highly cited publication proved to be influential in setting the research agenda internationally over the next decade. Many more opportunities to raise awareness would follow in subsequent years resulting from research projects which would in due course be awarded but, before that, IOM had to build capacity and capability.

Building capability: the Safety of Nanomaterials Independent Research Centre

Perhaps uniquely, certainly in the UK, IOM had highly relevant experience in both toxicology and assessment of exposure to very fine particles. However, IOM lacked the necessary resources to fully capitalise on the opportunity, having had almost no residual in-house practical toxicology capability since it had closed its pathology branch some years earlier. It had the knowledge of how to construct exposure scenarios and to measure exposure but lacked the equipment base to do that effectively for nanoparticles, since the necessary equipment was too expensive to allow a clear case for investment at that time. In order to provide credible responses to the research questions being posed, Tran and Aitken resolved to work with collaborators and build a multidisciplinary team which could attract funding and deliver work. Collaborations were set up with key partners including particle toxicologists Donaldson of Edinburgh University and Professor Vicki Stone of Napier University, and latterly Heriot Watt University, both long-term past collaborators with IOM. Another important early collaborator was Dr Qasim Chaudhry of the Central Science Laboratory in York, who brought special expertise in food safety. Eventually, these *ad hoc* collaborations were consolidated into more formal arrangements through the formation of the SnIRC (Safety of Nanomaterials Independent Research Centre) which became the core team for a series of projects carried out for UK Government departments. The SnIRC consortium proved to be an effective base from which to bid for and win key projects and to grow capability to do the work. At one point, more than fifty scientists in the four organisations were part of this group. From these beginnings, collaborations grew in the UK and across Europe, providing capacity to bid for larger pieces of work. This model was extended in Europe by the formation of the Nanosafetycluster, a community of scientists active in nanotechnology risk, in which IOM also played a leading role.[6]

Gathering the evidence: the first projects

In 2004, the Health and Safety Executive (HSE) invited IOM to bid to carry out a small review project to consider the implications of nanotechnology in the context of exposure and occupational hygiene.[7] The project was completed over a few months by a small team led by Aitken, including Tran and Dr Karen Galea, a young exposure scientist at IOM who had just completed her PhD at Aberdeen University. The resulting report was one of the first government-funded projects to address potential exposure to nanoparticles. Amongst the issues considered were known or anticipated usage of nanoparticles, possible exposure scenarios, potential numbers of exposed individuals, means and effectiveness of control measures, and gaps (in data and methods of assessment) and how these could be filled. The conclusion was that the knowledge and evidence base was inadequate for effective risk assessments.

Coming within months of the Royal Society report, this established IOM's credibility in relation to exposure to nanoparticles. Over the next few years, a series of projects was commissioned by various UK Government departments including Environment, Trade, Health and Safety and the Food Standards Agency, as part of their efforts to respond to the RS/RAEng report. Typically, these projects comprised evidence-gathering and review, presentation of that evidence to a group of scientists or peers, usually in the form of a workshop, an attempt to build consensus in that group, and finally a report with recommendations around the state of knowledge on the particular issue. The subject matters included nanomaterial usage and applications, hazard data needs, environmental regulation, food and food packaging, reference materials, cell penetration, high-aspect ratio particles, life-cycle assessment, and a review of ongoing research worldwide. This unique and extensive programme of work served to define the state of knowledge in the UK and was also influential worldwide on these issues in that decade.

SAFENANO: the UK Centre of Excellence in Nanosafety

In 2004, the UK Technology Strategy Board (TSB) approached IOM with a request to develop what would become the UK's Centre of Excellence in Nanosafety. Recognising that concern about risks could derail their investment in the Micro and Nanotechnology (MNT) programme, their mandate to IOM was to 'de-risk' the emerging UK nanotechnology industry.

Aitken, working with others at IOM including Tran and Peter Ritchie, Head of Information Technology, developed a proposal that was eventually funded by TSB and Scottish Enterprise (SE) to become one of the twenty-three MNT centres of excellence. Although the funding was modest in comparison to many of the other centres, it was nevertheless substantial, eventually rising to more than £0.5 million over a five-year period. The name SAFENANO was chosen to provide that clear identity and link to its purpose. Aitken took the lead as Director of the Centre and Stone was appointed Director of Toxicology, SAFENANO, consolidating the link to Edinburgh Napier University. The concept of SAFENANO had two elements. Firstly, it would be an independent, open and trusted source which collected and interpreted the emerging information to be used by industry, government, academia and the public. Secondly, it would provide services, based on the best available emerging standards, knowledge and practice, to help industry develop and use nanomaterials in a safe and responsible manner.

A communication strategy was developed. Bryony Ross, a young researcher with a strong interest in science communication, joined the team to provide additional resource. Central to the approach was an information-rich website, launched in 2005.[8] Ross was appointed SAFENANO's first editor. This unique site provided emerging information about exposure hazard and risk, guidance, news, and other knowledge-based resources. Maynard, in the USA, agreed to provide a weekly blog, a novel concept at that time. Industrial and academic partners provided other contributions. In parallel, SAFENANO launched social media streams on Twitter and LinkedIn, also very novel at that time, and established a regular newsletter which eventually attracted more than 1,000 subscribers.

In 2007, the growing SAFENANO team, now including Dr Steve Hankin, an expert in chemical risks, developed and launched a suite of laboratory- and field-based scientific services to support UK manufacturing and R&D, across industry and academic sectors. These included guidance for safe working practices, workplace assessments, toxicology testing, risk assessment and training. Importantly, this enabled IOM to build real capability and capacity to deliver field-based measurement services using state-of-the-art, real-time instruments. Around that time, Stone moved to Heriot Watt University, but continued in the role as Director of Toxicology of SAFENANO. This enabled the establishment of a toxicology laboratory with the recruitment of Dr Julia Varet, a young French toxicologist based full-time at Heriot Watt. Over the next few years, the SAFENANO team continued to grow with the recruitment of Dr Craig Poland, an outstanding young toxicologist, who had previously been a technician at IOM and had gone on to complete a PhD at Edinburgh University in Donaldson's group. Poland had already published a seminal and highly cited paper on the toxicology of carbon nanotubes.[9] Sheona Reid, a newly graduated chemist, and Gordon Fern, an experienced industrial chemist, also joined around that time.

Over the next few years SAFENANO grew rapidly. Hankin was appointed Director of Operations and SAFENANO established a model for working with innovation-led research projects which was subsequently exploited in European Framework Programmes FP7 and H2020. Other important projects in that time included one on Governance of Nanotechnology, for the European Chemical Industry Association, CEFIC, as well as numerous commercial projects. By 2019, the personnel involved had changed substantially but SAFENANO continues as a unique knowledge-based resource and has continued to develop an expanding range of commercial products and services to industry and academic clients, with a focus on understanding risk to support innovation.

Through these projects and its extensive and unique knowledge, IOM was established as the lead organisation in the UK for addressing nano-risk issues. However, whilst these projects were beneficial in gathering and interpreting existing evidence, they did not provide the necessary funding to carry out any new research in the area. Indeed, in the UK in general, funding for new research was in short supply. For this reason, Tran and Aitken looked to Europe to fund new research.

European research into safe use of nanomaterials
Assessing hazard and risk

In 2005, Tran won a bid to the EU Framework Programme 6 (FP6) for a project to develop a first structured assessment of the toxicological properties of nanomaterials. The project identified a set of five novel nanoparticles and assessed risks from exposure through air or the food supply, with a work programme integrating *in vitro* experiments, animal models of healthy/susceptible individuals and exposure/risk assessment.[10] Collaborators included Donaldson, Stone and Professor Wolfgang Kreyling in Germany. The project, tiny by EU Framework Project standards, was the first attempt to evaluate the toxicity of a set of nanoparticles in a systematic way and provided the first design of a framework to do this. This model was replicated in many subsequent projects funded in the FP7 and Horizon 2020 programmes. Major elements of this were improved particle characterisation, an assessment of the uses and application of the nanomaterials, consideration of exposure, toxicological assessment, usually *in vitro,* with an overall ambition to develop a risk framework for specific groups of nanomaterials.

Over the next few years, funding for nanotechnology risk research grew rapidly in Europe. Working in collaboration with international colleagues, IOM was able to win multiple research projects supporting further growth in IOM's capability and resources, as well as the opportunity to take forward its research agenda. Eventually whole programmes of nanotechnology risk research were established, at a European level, multiple projects being funded each year. In 2008 Tran, along with an international team of collaborators, won a project on risk assessment of engineered nanoparticles (ENPRA).[11] The funding of €3.7 million harnessed the knowledge and capabilities of fifteen European and six US partners including three US Federal Agencies. The project started with a launch event at the British Ambassador's residence in Paris, further raising the profile of the project and nanotechnology risk issues, and the reputation of IOM as a leader in this field [fig 9.3].

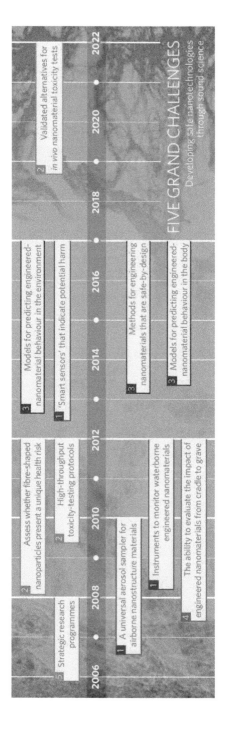

Fig 9.3: Five grand challenges for nanotechnology (Maynard et al. 2006)

Under Tran's leadership, this project utilised the latest advances in *in vitro*, *in vivo* and *in silico* approaches to nanotechnology safety research in order to realise its aims. The *in vitro* and *in silico* approaches developed help to reduce the need for animal experimentation in nanotoxicology. A multidisciplinary training school for new researchers was established in collaboration with the University of Venice, initially held on San Servolo, a beautiful island in the Venetian lagoon which was formerly an insane asylum. This training course has been further evolved and still runs each autumn in Venice, hundreds of researchers having now benefited from participation. ENPRA was followed in 2011 by MARINA, an even-larger project with more than forty partners, again led by Tran.[12] This was the largest nanotechnology risk project funded in Europe and was considered groundbreaking in that for the first time the full extent of the risk paradigm was addressed within a single project.

A link to nanomedicine

One developing area is nanomedicine. In 2017 IOM, under the leadership of Tran, won a major project in the EU Horizon 2020 Programme, to develop an integrated risk-management framework for nanobiomaterials used in advanced medicine and medical devices. The project will provide a ready-to-use and cost-efficient risk-management toolbox and decision support system, whereby validated tools and methods for materials, exposure, hazard and risk identification/assessment and management are integrated with a rationale for selecting and using them.

Gaps in knowledge about exposure

These and other projects highlighted a gap both in understanding about exposure to nanoparticles and also in availability of data on exposure. In 2009 IOM, led by Dr Martie van Tongeren who was, at the time, Head of the Exposure Group, obtained a grant, focusing on exposure of people to manufactured nanomaterials, with partners including Professors Michael Riediker at Institut Universitaire Romand de Santé au Travail (IST) Lausanne, and Derk Brouwer at TNO in the Netherlands.[13] This provided the first opportunity to develop an exposure assessment framework for nanomaterials. Fifty-seven exposure scenarios were developed based on data obtained from thirty-three literature references and from a number of large surveys. Unfortunately, the project still provided little opportunity to collect new exposure data. The performance of two common exposure models widely used by exposure and risk assessors showed no correlation between the model results and the results from the measurements.

These European projects and several others not described here had at their core the ambition to develop new methodologies, new techniques of toxicological or exposure assessment, and new frameworks by which that knowledge could be used to develop an effective risk assessment and management process for nanomaterials. In subsequent years, IOM's successes continued through a series of other projects focusing on multiple aspects of toxicology testing, exposure and risk assessment.

Taking a central role in European innovation: primary risk reduction in technological development

The main focus of the three European programmes, FP6, FP7 and H2020, was industrial innovation and transformation. Through these programmes, the EU was funding projects that were focused on developing new applications and uses of nanomaterials. Increasingly, as the programmes developed, the proposal calls referred to the need for projects to take account of risks as part of the innovation process. These innovation-led projects provided a second model and opportunity for IOM's research activities, based on the SAFENANO approach of using emerging knowledge of risk, to support innovation.

Risk reduction in innovation-led research

With this focus, IOM developed a new model to support a wide variety of innovation-led research: pro-actively assessing and managing risk in an integrated way, using the best available emerging knowledge supporting the main innovation programme. Typically, this was implemented as a risk work-package to sit alongside the main innovation process development. The key elements of this model looked at the potential risks at each stage of the innovation process along the value chain: design, material synthesis and manufacture, product incorporation, product use and end of life, and considered, in each stage possible exposures of people and the environment and the toxicity of the materials used. Risks were identified and where possible quantified and effective measures to manage those risks were developed.

The first of the projects was concerned with use of nanomaterials in the development of nanocomposites for use in lightweight structures in the wind-power and transport industries. The risk work-package considered plausible exposure scenarios, exposure measurement, toxicology and risk assessment, to estimate human health risks and develop preventive measures. There followed a series of other projects covering nanomaterial applications including graphene application in super capacitors, nanomaterials in polymer applications and nanoclays in packaging. Similar projects were developed supporting innovations based around new industrial processes. The risk-related outputs from these included methods for exposure assessment, good practice guides and better risk-control approaches. For IOM, this echoed an approach previously used in ergonomics research (see chapter 7), to support industrial development by ensuring that the innovation process was carried out in a safe and responsible way. Through these projects, IOM became much more closely integrated with industrial development and the application of new technology into products and services, a unique position within Europe.

Risk across the value chain

IOM's activities in these projects contributed to a developing concept that understanding risk across the value chain would remove barriers to innovation. This thinking is now well established within EU programmes. That idea was developed through a series of projects. The first of these, led by the Institute of Nanotechnology (ION), was set up to document and report on progress of technologies and applications of nanomaterials, the key output being a series of value nanotechnology chains. Within this, Aitken led a work-package on understanding associated nanotechnology risk, and through that was able to embed consideration of risks within the value chains. These ideas developed further in two other projects, one in which a virtual European technology platform was developed and another developing value chains for nano products. Again, Aitken developed and led health-risk work-packages in these projects. Although these projects were small, they were influential, and through them IOM achieved greater positioning with industry as the organisation within Europe that understood and had solutions for nanotechnology risk issues.

A role in advising on nanoregulation

A final group of European projects were based on improving regulation. In 2011, Aitken was approached to join a consortium led by Tom van Teunenbroek, a Dutch ministry official, and others who were attempting to put together a project led by national ministries to develop a common European approach to the regulatory testing of nanomaterials. Out of these discussions came the NANoREG project, the scale of which dwarfed all previous EU projects.[14] The total estimated budget was in excess of €50 million of which 90% was provided by national governments. IOM was appointed, with the support of the UK Environment Department (DEFRA), as the UK coordinator with a total budget of €700K. Within the project, van Tongeren led the exposure work-package. The aim was to provide definitive answers to a set of regulatory questions, posed by national ministries. The results were published in a 'white paper' that provides recommendations for policymakers and regulators aimed at a more effective and cost-efficient assessment of nanomaterials in a regulatory context.[15] Amongst others, the recommendations include proposals for measures such as further harmonisation of test methods by the OECD, and proposals for a more efficient use of the results of nanosafety projects by improving the data management infrastructure. Other recommendations were aimed at making European chemical hazard regulations (REACH) more readily applicable to nanomaterials. For the long term, some possibilities for innovation in risk assessment were presented, aimed at speeding up the process of risk assessment, reducing costs and reducing animal testing. The project also introduced the concept of 'Safe by Design' for nanomaterials, an ideal which is gaining further ground.[16] Finally, the white paper introduced a recommendation for more future-proof approaches to secure the safety of current and next-generation nanomaterials. Despite these and other intensive efforts, approaching the end of the current EU programmes, many gaps remain, implying the need for further work.

Standardisation, guidance and regulation

A further critical contribution by IOM was in standardisation. Early in the development of nanotechnology opportunities, it was recognised that a lack of common nomenclature and methodologies was severely restricting their application. In the UK, the British Standards Institute (BSI) was tasked to develop a standardisation initiative in nanotechnology. Aitken was invited to join a BSI committee under the chairmanship of Dr Peter Hatto to draft what became the first vocabulary standard for nanoparticles in 2005.[17] This was the first document published by a national standards body in which definitions of terms such as 'nanotechnology', 'nanoparticle', 'nanotube', as well as 'engineered' and 'incidental nanoparticles' were developed. Following this, BSI established a National Standards Committee for Nanotechnology (NTI/1) and an International Standards Committee (ISO 229), both chaired by Hatto. Aitken joined both as the UK lead expert on health and safety.

In 2006, BSI commissioned IOM to develop the 'British Standard Guide for Safe Handling and Disposal of Nanomaterials'. This document, published as BSI 6699-2 in 2007, provided a basic framework to manage these risks.[18] Despite being praised in Parliament by the Minister for Science and Innovation, Ian Pearson, this proved to be a controversial document.[19] It contained a first attempt to group nanomaterials into four hazard-based categories for the purposes of risk assessment, and made recommendations about 'plausible' benchmark exposure levels (BELs) appropriate for each category. The limitations of this approach were acknowledged, stating that the standard was a pragmatic attempt to fill what had been identified as a serious gap, namely, that evidence strongly suggested that nanoparticles were more hazardous than 'conventional sized materials'. This implied that occupational exposure limits based on conventional sized materials could no longer be considered sufficiently protective. The document was heavily criticised for having insufficient evidence to support the BELs and so was never fully approved by HSE. Nevertheless, eleven years later BSI 6699-2 remains freely available from BSI and has not been updated, and similar approaches have been developed in several other European countries.

In 2009, IOM with partners was successful in bidding for two consultancy projects commissioned by the European Commission to develop improved guidance for nanomaterials in REACH guidance documents.[20] The remit was to review and develop recommendations concerning information requirements and chemical safety requirements in REACH for nanomaterials. Two final reports were produced: 'Information Requirements' and 'Chemical Safety Assessment'. Based on the scientific and technical state-of-the-art recommendations in these reports, the European Chemicals Agency on 30 April 2012 published three new appendices to its 'Guidance on Information Requirements and Chemical Safety Assessment'. These are now the recommendations for registering nanomaterials.

Singapore

IOM's work in nanotechnology was the critical factor in the establishment of IOM Singapore. In 2008, Aitken visited Singapore and held a meeting with the Singapore Economic Development Board (EDB) to discuss their plans for nanotechnology development and their concerns about nanotechnology risk. Following that initial meeting, discussions were held over the next few years, culminating in 2012 in an agreement with EDB, negotiated by Aitken and Phil Woodhead, IOM's Chief Executive, in which EDB committed to provide a grant to enable IOM to open an office in Singapore. Specifically, EDB wanted IOM to make the SAFENANO model available as a principal service offering, effectively replicating the SAFENANO mission for the Department of Trade and Industry in the UK. IOM Singapore opened on 1 September 2012 with an office in Chevron House in Raffles Place. Aitken relocated to Singapore to become IOM Singapore's first Managing Director. His wife, Kathleen Aitken, was appointed as Office Manager. Michael Riediker, a long-standing collaborator from Switzerland who had worked with Aitken on previous EU projects, was appointed as SAFENANO Director of Operations, IOM Singapore.

Developing research

The primary ambition of IOM Singapore was to build a portfolio of consultancy and service work. However, it became clear almost from the start that there was also an opportunity for research work on nanotechnology risk in Singapore. The approach used to develop that work was to repurpose research previously done in Europe and the UK into a Singapore context. Discussions were held with government agencies and interested researchers in national universities and institutes in the country. An important strategy, similar to that used earlier in the UK, was to build collaborations with other, established, researchers in Singapore around nano-risk issues and to prepare collaborative proposals. Riediker and Aitken set about making friends.

The first success was with the Workplace Safety and Health Institute (WSHI) who commissioned a project to identify and assess usage of nanomaterials in Singapore and the readiness of the emerging Singapore nanotechnology industry to address potential risks. This project was led by Riediker, and Professor Ng Kee Woie, a research leader at the National Technical University (NTU), was a partner. A young researcher, Dr Yu Ting from mainland China, who had completed his PhD at NTU, joined IOM staff to work full-time on this project. The project demonstrated a lack of awareness of risk issues among the emerging industries that were using nanomaterials in Singapore and showed a clear need to develop better guidance (and more encouragement).

At the same time, Aitken and Riediker pitched an idea to the Public Utilities Board (PUB) about a project to assess the possible risks to the water system in Singapore from nanomaterials in commercial products such as personal care products and paints. Water quality is a strategic issue in Singapore owing to the limited land area for rainfall collection and the need for recycling. This project was funded in 2013 and another full-time researcher, Dr Zhang Yuan Yuan who had completed her PhD at the National University of Singapore, was recruited. The project demonstrated a small but significant potential for nanoparticles to enter the water supply. This led to a follow-up project to look at nanoparticle detection methods in water. These projects allowed IOM Singapore to grow staff numbers and capability. However, as had been seen in Europe, the appetite for industry to engage consultancy support on risks around nanotechnology was quite limited. IOM did establish good and lasting relationships with several small enterprises, supporting them in setting up good practice at the start of commercial production. These relationships continue, as does work with a growing number of private client companies.

Raising the profile

Further work to raise the profile of nanotechnology risks in Singapore continued. Aitken joined what was initially an *ad hoc* Singapore Standards Committee on nanotechnology and persuaded them to take forward the development of a Singapore standard on safe use of nanomaterials. Riediker successfully organised (on a commercial basis) two international conferences on Risk Analysis in 2015 and Particle Toxicology in 2016 in Singapore. In 2016 Riediker and Aitken set up a collaboration between Singapore-based researchers with an aim to develop research opportunities and to push the research agenda in Singapore.[21] One outcome was an invitation to participate in a joint research programme between NTU and Harvard University on responsible nanotechnology, under the leadership of Ng Kee Woie at NTU. That led to a research project on exposure of printers to nanoparticles, now led in Singapore by Sriram Prasath, IOM's research lead.

In 2016, Aitken returned to the UK to take up the position of Chief Executive at IOM. In 2018, Riediker also returned to Europe to establish a consultancy business in Switzerland. However, both remain active working with Prasath to develop research and consultancy opportunities there. A key strategy is to have more collaboration between researchers in the UK and Singapore.

Future prospects for safe use of nanotechnology

Since 2002, the knowledge and the landscape has changed substantially. Over the last fifteen years there has been a significant global investment in nanosafety research. The EU contribution to this field of research over the past twelve years, through funding via research programmes, has been about €400 million.[14] Member States have also invested a similar amount in funding research into nano-environment health and safety assessment. US spend is likely to be as high, leading to an overall estimate of greater than €1 billion.

This extensive worldwide research effort has resulted in the generation of an enormous quantity of scientific data on toxicology, exposure and risk. Despite this investment, definitive answers to some of the fundamental questions posed at the start of this activity have been slow to emerge. Reasons for this may include the multiplicity of nanomaterials, a lack of clear evidence of health effects in humans (thankfully), an increasing reluctance to conduct *in vivo* toxicity studies and deficits in available exposure data.

However, progress is being made. While there are no novel adverse effects observed, nanomaterials *can* trigger the adverse effects (e.g. inflammation, fibrosis) at lower mass dose in comparison to the larger materials of identical composition. Thus, with a set of appropriate dose-metrics (surface area), it is possible to describe the dose-response of nanomaterials consistently, from large to nano-sized materials.

Much more is now known on the different toxicity of types of carbon nanotubes (CNT) and the mechanisms which govern these effects. It is now possible to a much greater degree to group different nanoparticles according to the level of hazard that they present, based on physicochemical properties. More is also known about the likelihood of release of nanoparticles into the air for different scenarios across the value chain and how to sample and measure them in the air if release occurs. Better guidance tools, such as control banding, which can be used to define appropriate methods to manage the risks are also available.

There are now many examples of responsible, pragmatic industry practice addressing these risk issues in a proactive way. Evidence-based proportional governance has emerged most notably in Europe, where specific guidance pertaining to nanomaterials in relation to chemicals regulations such as REACH has now been published (following on from specific regulatory requirements for cosmetics and food). And yet there are other examples where government, academia and industry have still fully to recognise the extent of the risk issues and have not yet put in place the necessary steps to manage them effectively.

In all of these matters, IOM has been a major contributor. By any measure, IOM's work on nanotechnology risk must be considered a huge success. It demonstrated that, by taking a highly energetic proactive approach, it was possible to raise the profile of a whole area of science, build capacity and credibility for IOM, and move the international agenda. Beyond the scientific contribution, it has enabled IOM to raise its profile in the UK, Europe and Asia, to build capability and resources, to recruit new staff with new skills in toxicology and exposure, and to establish itself as a leading organisation in what are key emerging technologies. It has enabled IOM to develop in innovative ways, from new ideas about science communication, and to think in a new paradigm about our research being key to supporting innovation. EU programmes have been exceptionally successful for IOM. In terms of participation, IOM was the leading organisation in the UK in Nano-Environment Health and Safety projects in FP7 and in the top five in Europe. In FP7 IOM won twenty-four projects with a total value (to IOM) of over €6 million. Based largely (although not solely) on nano projects, WHO reported that IOM was the fifth most active participating organisation on environment and health in FP7, eclipsing organisations such as Imperial College and TNO.[22] (These numbers exclude the innovation-led projects.) This success continued into H2020, where up until 2018, seven further projects with a total value of over €4 million were won. These are extraordinary achievements for an organisation the size of IOM, and are a great tribute to the energy and commitment of the people involved and quality of the work done.

Nanomedicine provides a possible pathway for IOM to develop its capability further into biomedical applications. If that can be realised, it will extend IOM's possibilities for expansion from enabling and supporting innovations to providing solutions. Going forward, the skills, experience and the position which has been achieved across all of nanotechnology provide a strong basis for future success in this area and a model to be exploited in other emerging technologies and emerging risks.

There is still much work to be done and IOM is very well placed to do it. The nano story still has many years to run.

Chapter 9: References and Notes

1. European Commission 2002; The Sixth Framework Programme (FP6) in brief. https://ec.europa.eu/research/fp6/pdf/fp6-in-brief_en.pdf

   European Framework Programmes are large multi-year programmes which provide the frame for EU activities in the field of science, research and innovation. FP6 had a budget of €17.5 billion for the years 2002-06 representing about 4 to 5% of the overall expenditure on R&D in EU Member States. The main objective of FP6 was to contribute to the creation of the European Research Area (ERA) by improving integration and co-ordination of research in Europe. At the same time the research was targeted at strengthening the competitiveness of the European economy, solving major societal questions and supporting the formulation and implementation of other EU policies. Activities under Framework Programmes have to be conducted in compliance with ethical principles, including those reflected in the Charter of Fundamental Rights of the European Union as well as increasing the role of women in research and improving information for, and dialogue with, society. Subsequent Framework Programmes were FP7 and Horizon 2020 (H2020).

2. Tran CL, Buchanan D, Cullen RT, Searl A, Jones AD, Donaldson K. (2000). Inhalation of poorly soluble particles. II. Influence of particle surface area on inflammation and clearance. *Inhalation Toxicology*; 12: 1113-1126. doi: 10.1080/08958370050166796.

3. Seaton A, MacNee W, Donaldson K, Godden D. (1995). Particulate air pollution and acute health effects. *Lancet*; 345(8943): 176-178.

4. The Royal Society and Royal Academy of Engineering's report on nanotechnologies – Nanoscience and nanotechnologies: opportunities and uncertainties. https://royalsociety.org/topics-policy/publications/2004/nanoscience-nanotechnologies/

5. Maynard AD, Aitken RJ, Butz T, Colvin V, Donaldson K, Oberdorster G, Philbert MA, Ryan J, Seaton A, Stone V, Tinkle SS, Tran L, Walker NJ, Warheit DB. (2006). Safe handling of nanotechnology. *Nature*; 444: 267-268. https://www.nature.com/articles/444267a

6. Nanosafetycluster website https://www.nanosafetycluster.eu/

7. Aitken RJ, Creely KS, Tran CL. (2004). Nanoparticles: an occupational hygiene review. Sudbury: HSE Books. (RR274).

8. SAFENANO website https://www.safenano.org/

9. Poland CA, Duffin R, Kinloch I, Maynard A, Wallace WAH, Seaton A, Stone V, Brown S, MacNee W, Donaldson K. (2008). Carbon nanotubes introduced into the abdominal cavity of mice show asbestos-like pathogenicity in a pilot study. *Nature Nanotechnology* (epub 20 May 2008). http://www.nature.com/articles/nnano.2008.111

10. PARTICLE-RISK https://cordis.europa.eu/project/rcn/74743/factsheet/en

11. ENPRA (Risk Assessment of Engineered NanoParticles) website http://www.enpra.eu/

12. MARINA (Managing Risks of Nanomaterials) website http://www.marina-fp7.eu/

13. NanEX publishable summary http://www.nanex-project.eu/

mainpages/public-documents/doc_download/100-nanex-project-publishable-summary.pdf

14. NANoREG – A common European approach to the regulatory testing of manufactured nanomaterials website http://www.nanoreg.eu/

15. ProSafe. (2017). The ProSafe white paper: Towards a more effective and efficient governance and regulation of nanomaterials. Web published: ProSafe Project Office. https://www.rivm.nl/sites/default/files/2018-11/ProSafe%20White%20Paper%20updated%20version%2020170922.pdf

16. Note: Safe by design (SbD). The concept of safety by design is to preferably eliminate, and if not eliminate to control, health and safety risks in engineering projects and processes by early consideration of potential risks and then deal with those risks at the design stage. Attempts are now being made to apply this concept to chemicals and to nanomaterials.

17. British Standards Institution. (2005). PAS 71:2005 Vocabulary. Nanoparticles. London: BSI.

18. British Standards Institution. (2007). PD 6699-2 Nanotechnologies – Part 2: Guide to safe handling and disposal of manufactured nanomaterials. London: BSI.

19. Note: On 21 February 2008, Ian Pearson, Minister of State (Minister for Science and Innovation) in the Department for Innovation, Universities and Skills (DIUS) made a statement in response to a parliamentary question from Rob Marris, Member of Parliament for Wolverhampton South West: "To ask the Secretary of State… what discussions he has had with the Health and Safety Executive on health and safety standards in nanotechnology research development". Pearson stated, "The Government are committed to understanding any potential risks of nanotechnologies and to managing them within a proportionate regulatory framework". Regarding BSI PD 6699-2 – Guide to Safe Handling and Disposal of Manufactured Nanomaterials, Pearson stated, "[it] provides advice on good

practice to those working in laboratories where research on new materials and applications is being undertaken, as this is where exposure to engineered free nanoscale materials is most likely to occur at present".

20. Note: REACH is a European Union regulation concerning the Registration, Evaluation, Authorisation and Restriction of Chemicals. It came into force on 1 June 2007 and replaced a number of European Directives and Regulations with a single system. REACH (EC 1907/2006) aims to improve the protection of human health and the environment through the better and earlier identification of the intrinsic properties of chemical substances. REACH also aims to enhance innovation and competitiveness of the EU chemicals industry. Manufacturers and importers are required to gather information on the properties of their chemical substances, which will allow their safe handling, and to register the information in a central database in the European Chemicals Agency (ECHA) in Helsinki. The Agency is the central point in the REACH system: it manages the databases necessary to operate the system, co-ordinates the in-depth evaluation of suspicious chemicals and is building up a public database in which consumers and professionals can find hazard information. REACH guidance describes the information requirements under REACH with regard to substance properties, exposure, use and risk management measures, in the context of the chemical safety assessment. These documents aim to help all stakeholders with their preparation for fulfilling their obligations under the REACH Regulation.

21. nanOsing website http://nanosing.sg/

22. World Health Organization. (2015). Improving environment and health in Europe: how far have we gotten? Copenhagen: WHO Regional Office for Europe.

Part 3

Looking to the Future

10

Lessons from the past: drawing together the threads

Summary

IOM's history provides many valuable lessons to inform its future success. Of overriding importance has been a commitment to practical and applied science with the purpose of improving health of workers and the wider population. Understanding and managing the risks from particles has been a central theme but the need to adapt both the topics addressed and the methods used has been critical to success. Evolution of the organisational structure with emphasis on different types and models of funded work at different times has been necessary to ensure IOM's continued existence. Underpinning all of IOM's work has been its enduring commitment to its values of independence, impartiality, integrity, quality and sustainability. However, nothing could have been achieved without the extraordinary efforts and endeavours of its staff, many of whom have devoted decades of their working lives to the organisation, its science and its provision of services.

As many throughout history have commented, to understand the future it is necessary to examine the past. IOM is an organisation with a great history. For fifty years, it has been at the forefront of research to understand and mitigate a range of occupational and environmental health risks from coal dust to asbestos to carbon nanotubes to air pollution. What then, are the lessons for IOM?

IOM's approach to science

The 13th-century English philosopher Roger Bacon is quoted as saying, "To ask the proper question is half of knowing".

In 1969, when IOM was founded, its work was entirely focused on the coal industry and it started with two, apparently simple, questions:

* How much and what kinds of dust cause pneumoconiosis?
* What dust level in mines needs to be maintained if men are to be prevented from becoming disabled?

These surely have been proper questions for IOM to address on its fifty-year journey. In trying answers to these questions, IOM has evolved and changed in many different ways. Its work now extends well beyond the coal industry into an ever-increasing range of industries, environments and populations with very different agents of ill health and health outcomes. However, these two founding questions, adapted and generalised for different health risks and contexts, have remained central to why IOM exists. They have defined its purpose and its work.

Throughout its years of existence, IOM has expressed its purpose in different ways at different times but most recently as follows:

"Our purpose is to improve people's health and safety at work, at home and in the environment through excellent independent science to create a healthy and sustainable world".[1]

This objective has been approached by creating and advancing knowledge through scientific research and analysis and by applying this knowledge to support policy and practice development. IOM has used knowledge to develop and deliver consultancy and services and to raise levels of awareness and understanding of current and emerging health, safety and wellbeing issues with government, industry and the public. In doing this, it has developed the capacity to be a sustainable business. In line with its ethos as stated in chapter 2, it has been important that the work is not only interesting but is also of value to society. IOM has not been engaged in science simply to find and refine ever-more detailed answers to academic questions. Rather, its objective has always been the application of science, making a difference in both policy and practice. Science with purpose.

Usually, but particularly in larger projects, IOM has worked across many scientific disciplines. In its early years this was a novel approach. Indeed, it may reasonably be claimed that IOM was one of the first organisations in its field to work in this way. This approach came from the earliest days of the research into coal workers' pneumoconiosis when it was apparent that knowledge of engineering, exposure to dust, toxicology, statistics and epidemiology as well as medical understanding were *all* necessary to address the questions IOM was seeking to answer. Answers from single disciplines were incomplete and ineffective. This led to a working methodology based on multidisciplinary project teams. As a result, most of the senior scientists involved from the beginning acquired a broad grasp of several sciences as well as their own specialty. It is interesting that current thinking in research funding strongly promotes multidisciplinary research for these very reasons.

Where additional expertise was required, collaboration with other organisations has been a key approach. This has been exemplified most clearly in IOM's European research projects where large multidisciplinary, internationally based teams often including dozens of partner organisations have been constructed to answer increasingly complex questions. IOM has been good at building teams, good at building collaborations and getting these collaborations to work together effectively to deliver the results.

Throughout its lifetime, IOM has had a strong focus on the risks of particles. This theme has been a consistent thread running through its work for the last fifty years, and has moved IOM from coal mining to nanotechnology, from 19th-century to 21st-century disruptive technologies, and from miners' diseases to population effects of air pollution. Particle risks remain a relevant issue, but many other health risks have been addressed including carcinogenesis, human and behavioural factors, musculoskeletal injury, and wider public health issues. IOM is well equipped to adapt to changes in the modern ambient and workplace environments.

The importance of IOM's values

IOM's values of independence, impartiality, integrity, quality and sustainability underpin both its work and the confidence that its clients place in the answers that it gives. IOM never deviates from these values. It gives the best scientific and evidence-based opinion regardless of who pays and whether the results seem favourable or not. This has enabled IOM to establish a strong position as a trusted voice valued by industry, government, academia and the wider public. This consistency of approach has been a hallmark of IOM's work over the fifty years.

When the National Coal Board established IOM, the need for independence was recognised at the outset. The principle that IOM should publish its research, regardless of who funded it or whether the results seemed favourable or not, was an explicit requirement. Since then IOM has received funding from many sources, including national governments, agencies, industry and research funding organisations, but that requirement has remained. In the wider environment, many scientists now face challenges relating to who is funding their research. Critics sometimes imply, usually in an attempt to discredit the work, that where 'interested parties' fund research, these parties will have some influence over the results.

This is not a view held in IOM. However, it is nevertheless critical to guard against any such inference. For that reason, IOM's right to publish its work has been defended ferociously. On very rare occasions, where the right to publish has not been agreeable at the outset, it has been necessary to refuse to take on a contract. On some occasions there have been conflicts with clients who have found the results to be unexpected or uncomfortable. Fortunately, this has occurred rarely; when it has, the objections have been challenged, overcome and the work published.

The commercial work that IOM does is not intended for publication in the public domain. However, IOM is equally fastidious in the need to give clients the results and explain clearly their context and interpretation, to ensure they are used appropriately and not misrepresented. Being independent does not preclude IOM and IOM staff from having opinions, but independence means that these opinions must be expressed in a way that is consistent with IOM's values. IOM's opinion cannot be bought or influenced by others.

People are at the heart of all we do

IOM has benefited from having highly committed, effective and driven people who have, in many cases, spent the greater part of their working life upholding its values and delivering on its mission. Many of IOM's staff, past and present, are internationally recognised as leading thinkers in their subject areas. This includes a significant number of people who have begun their careers as technicians and gone on to complete PhDs. Many others have made equally effective and important contributions without the external recognition. IOM has provided the platform for many hundreds of individuals to develop their careers and take forward science for the benefit of all.

Differences in the requirements and expectations between commercial and research clients, in terms of cost, timescales, reporting and level of detail required, has led to different demands on the people who have to deliver the work. This has sometimes led to different views of how best to organise and what norms in terms of behaviours, quality and attitudes are necessary to meet those requirements.

These tensions are perhaps inevitable, but what has been important in recent years is to recognise that these differences do exist and to work through them to address the fragmentation caused. All of IOM's people are important, valued and contribute to its central purpose.

Innovation is a fundamental need

In any business, even highly successful ones, there is a life cycle associated with products or services that moves from launch to growth, maturity and decline. Even excellent products will eventually decline as the market changes or new products are introduced to replace them. This applies equally to IOM's research and services. Had IOM limited its interest to coal and the risks from coal dust it would not have survived. As the key questions were answered and the coal industry declined (at least in the UK and Europe) the need for IOM's work on that topic and the funders willing to pay for it also declined. A similar example was IOM's asbestos surveying business. IOM was an early entrant into that business and was able to grow rapidly as that market grew. As the market evolved from an expert-led model to commoditised services, the price model changed to the extent that IOM could no longer earn the revenues required to continue. Ultimately, this led to a decision to divest that business. There are many other examples within the IOM story which demonstrate this evolution. As this history demonstrates, for IOM to survive it has had to innovate and evolve, to extend its range and scope and to build new capabilities and revenue streams.

Innovation is usually described in terms of radical or incremental innovation. A radical (or disruptive) innovation is one that has a significant impact on a market and on the economic activity of an organisation in that market, while incremental innovation concerns an existing product, service, process or method whose performance has been significantly enhanced or upgraded. IOM can point to examples of both which have enabled it to survive and grow. These include the highly successful innovations that IOM has developed, such as in the ergonomics of machine design, the improvement of dust samplers, prevention of risk in nanotechnologies, and design and testing of hospital ventilation.

In innovation, however, not everything is successful. With limited reserves for investment there is a tendency towards 'being sure' before launching any new initiatives in case they are not successful. Prudence is appropriate but there is a case for IOM to be bolder in innovating to expand its scope and offering. Even where new initiatives are not successful, this should not be considered a failure. What is important is to learn from this and improve next time. No part of IOM's business is immune from changes in the market. The challenge is to reshape and evolve so that IOM meets (and in some cases drives) the market, be it in research or services, with an offering that ultimately provides a solution for the client.

A secure financial basis is critical

The challenge to remain financially secure has been continuous throughout IOM's existence. Since IOM receives no core funding from any other organisation, all its work and operating costs need to come from revenues received from clients. When IOM became fully financially independent from British Coal in 1990, decisions were taken to establish a more financially secure position. This meant taking a more commercial, business-like approach to all its work, with more effective budgeting, planning and management, and expanding the commercial work to provide a more robust financial base going forward. A subsidiary company, IOM

Consulting, was formed to allow the commercial entity to trade profitably within the overall charitable framework of IOM. This strategy was successful and revenues grew in the decades that followed, enabling IOM to survive and to some extent prosper. Profits were made in some years and reinvested, while reserves were sufficient to cover losses in the other years. Opportunities were developed and taken, difficult decisions about the size and shape of the organisation were faced and made. Along the way, IOM managed to move to a new purpose-built headquarters on Heriot Watt Science Park and to open new offices in Stafford, Chesterfield, London and Singapore. Overall, IOM's financial position remains sufficiently secure to give confidence of future success but sufficiently challenging to ensure that there can be no relaxation in efforts to improve it.

Future directions

Summary

The world of work is changing dramatically, not only with respect to industries themselves but also to the types of jobs, employment models and variations across the world. Maintenance of good health is recognised as one of the most important global challenges, and environmental risk factors, in the workplace or the wider human environment, provide the most important opportunities for prevention of ill health. The boundaries between workplace, environment and public health are increasingly blurred, but the evidence of environmental risks to health is becoming more clearly defined. IOM's science and approach to quantification and reduction of risk are highly appropriate to addressing these issues; to continue its success it must evolve to ensure it remains relevant and able to deliver world-class science and scientific services. With the continued commitment of its people, it is determined to deliver its purpose to "improve people's health and safety at work, at home and in the environment through excellent independent science, to create a healthy and sustainable world".

The Nobel-winning physicist Niels Bohr is quoted as saying *"Prediction is very difficult, especially if it is about the future"*. In truth, had anyone fifty years ago tried to predict the size, shape, scope and workload of the current IOM, it would have been impossible. Nevertheless, as an organisation moving into the future, it is necessary to have a vision of the direction and a strategy by which it will get there, even though these plans and strategies will certainly change in their execution.

Emerging problems and opportunities

IOM is concerned primarily with the prevention of ill health and the promotion of good health. Maintenance of health is one of the most fundamental and important global challenges, and many of these relate to environmental risk factors, be they in the workplace or the wider human environment.

The world of work is changing dramatically including changes to industries, the types of jobs, employment models and regional variations across the world. In the West in particular, there is a decline in employment in manufacturing and extractive industries, and an increase in what is thought of as office work, although it is not always done in an office. Increasingly people work at home, in shared informal spaces and on the move. The emergence of a 24/7 culture has disrupted traditional patterns of work-life balance and social support mechanisms. The use of artificial intelligence, big data, robotics and the internet of things is growing rapidly. Millions of people spend their entire working day in front of a computer, tablet, smartphone or other interface device.

There are fewer large companies, lots of small to medium enterprises, and many millions of self-employed individuals. People change their jobs and careers many times in their working life. There is a huge rise in the 'gig' economy, in which people have temporary jobs or are doing separate pieces of work, each paid separately, rather than working for an employer on a regular contract. There is much more part-time working. As western economies age, so retirement age increases leading to an ageing workforce with increased vulnerabilities, often managing chronic disease or reduced mobilities. Hazards in the modern workplace can also relate to the way that work is organised rather than specific agents, and the consequential harm may be more psychological than physical.

Construction is growing rapidly, particularly in developing economies, often with new techniques and materials. In industrial, scientific and high-technology manufacturing, people may be exposed to new potential hazards such as nanomaterials and biologically modified materials, as well as having long-term low-level exposures to other chemicals and materials. In developing economies, millions are still employed in extraction, construction and manufacturing, often in conditions which have become rare or even absent in the West. Exposure to dust and asbestos is still a major issue and agriculture remains a huge and dangerous occupation worldwide.

Infectious diseases remain a threat but now in most countries morbidity and mortality in adults are dominated by non-communicable disease (NCD), including heart disease, cancer, diabetes and chronic musculoskeletal and respiratory diseases. Environmental pollution is now recognised as one of the most important causes of death and disease. According to WHO, in terms of global disease burden, over one-third of deaths from stroke, lung cancer and chronic respiratory disease, and one-quarter of deaths from ischaemic heart disease may be attributable to the effects of air pollution, with more that 6 million deaths attributed to this annually. Climate change, the greatest current threat to civilisation, is now also recognised as a major contributory factor to ill health, for example from displacement of people by drought and flooding. In public health, chronic diseases, strongly linked to diet, physical activity, and tobacco and alcohol consumption, have increased dramatically. The burden of diseases such as heart disease, stroke, cancer, diabetes and asthma is now heaviest in low- and middle-income countries.

The United Nations Sustainable Development Goals (SDGs) call on countries to mobilise efforts to end all forms of poverty, fight inequalities and tackle climate change, while ensuring that no one country is left behind. They recognise that ending poverty must go hand-in-hand with strategies that build economic growth and address a range of social needs including education, health, social protection and job opportunities, while tackling climate change and protecting a diverse environment.

The increasingly complex world of work taken with the fact that most ill health in individuals has multiple contributory causes has changed the concept, still widely believed, that most diseases have a single cause, and this has led to the concept of investigation of risk factors for disease. In occupational and environmental medicine, this implies discovering what the main risk factors are and then acting to reduce them in populations, be they workforces or those of towns and cities. For example, the main causes of ill health in the workplace are musculoskeletal and psychological problems; both have obvious risk factors in work and at home or at leisure. Prevention depends on both individual and environmental action.

In responding to these complex issues, potential clients including government agencies and industries increasingly are looking for support to move from developing or refining the evidence of harm to provision and implementation of solutions. This trend is particularly apparent in developing economies where, having recognised that there are problems, the focus now is to prevent them by using the best available methods.

Vision for the future

The world is changing rapidly, perhaps more rapidly than at any time in IOM's history. In response, IOM must continue to adapt and evolve to remain relevant, add value and realise its purpose. IOM's vision is to remain a globally recognised organisation that engages and empowers its staff to deliver its mission of contributing to a healthy and sustainable world.

In September 2018, in response to these challenges, IOM launched a new strategy, '*IOM 2018-2023 – A strategy for success*' to refocus its purpose and vision, refresh its values and to clarify three strategic aims.[1] These aims are based on IOM's science, people and finance, underpinned by IOM's values driven by innovation [fig 11.1].

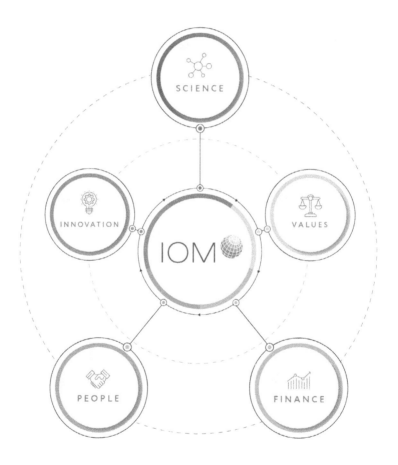

Fig 11.1: Science, values, finance, people and innovation, the elements that safeguard IOM

The first aim relates to science: *To maximise the relevance, benefits and impact of our work.* Through its science, IOM will look to focus on key risk issues of importance. This includes a deliberate extension to the scope of its work with an increased emphasis on environmental and public health topics such as pollution, climate change, urban health and sustainability. It is these areas where perhaps the greatest numbers of people may be suffering the consequences of exposure to hazardous agents. In these cases, environmental pollution drives the health effects. As part of this shift, IOM is deliberately aligning its research more coherently with the UN Sustainable Development Goals.[2]

However, IOM must also consolidate and develop its existing areas of occupational and workplace health, exposure science, nanotechnology, citizen science, human factors and wellbeing. Within these areas, new topics are emerging such as shiftwork and cancer, dementia in professional sports people and robotics and automation, where IOM is already beginning to work and achieve prominence. The international dimension of IOM's work is also important, since the issues it addresses are worldwide. IOM already leads projects or does work in Europe, Asia and the USA. IOM's base in Singapore provides a further opportunity for expanding work across Asia and into China in particular.

To increase the impact of its work, IOM will implement more effective and deliberate communication including raising awareness and profile; influencing policy and practice; providing training; and building strategic collaborations and partnerships. However, perhaps the greatest opportunity to increase the impact of IOM's work lies in the development and implementation of solutions. This requires a greater research focus 'downstream' on making change happen. IOM must optimise how it uses its research and other knowledge to develop new products and services and translate research into practice, with more focus on implementing policy, creating change and making a positive difference to people's lives. The future IOM needs to emphasise its long-standing interest in not only identifying and evaluating solutions but also providing them.

The second aim relates to people: *to develop a stimulated committed workforce with the capacity to deliver.* IOM is committed to organisational development, to build an open, inclusive culture based on mutual trust and respect, for each other, for the work we do, for our customers and wider stakeholders, ensuring that all play their part. IOM staff actively work together, collaborating and encouraging continuous learning and improvement across the organisation including ongoing review of its systems and processes, adopting new technologies and leadership development at all levels.

The third aim relates to finance. It is: *To secure financial sustainability.* IOM must aim to secure financial suitability, growing revenues by sustaining and investing in successful areas, supporting recovery in underperforming areas, and improving the product and service mix and its focus on high value. It must also ensure it has the effective and efficient business processes and organisational structures to deliver its objectives.

This strategy and the plans through which it will be implemented provide a roadmap for the future development of IOM and is a good start for the next fifty years. However, the success or otherwise of IOM over the next fifty years will depend on many factors which cannot be known at this point. IOM's two basic questions of how much and what kinds of exposure cause health effects and what levels of exposure need to be maintained to prevent health effects occurring still seem to be highly relevant. To this can be added a third, implied but not stated in the original two: how can these levels be achieved and maintained? In providing answers to these questions, there is a great opportunity for IOM's contribution to continue and grow, building on what has already been achieved. Future success will depend on IOM's ability to innovate, be relevant and add value. If this can be achieved IOM surely will fulfil its purpose to *improve people's health and safety at work, at home and in the environment through excellent independent science, to create a healthy and sustainable world.* IOM, science with purpose.

Chapter 11: References and Notes

1. IOM Strategy https://www.iom-world.org/media/1256/2018-2023-strategyforsuccess_final.pdf

2. The United Nations Sustainable Development Goals are a collection of seventeen global goals set by the United Nations General Assembly in 2015. The Sustainable Development Goals are the blueprint to achieve a better and more sustainable future for all. They address the global challenges we face, including those related to poverty, inequality, climate, environmental degradation, prosperity, and peace and justice. The Goals interconnect and, in order to leave no one behind, it is important to achieve each Goal and target by 2030.

   More information is available at https://www.un.org/sustainabledevelopment/sustainable-development-goals/

Index of acronyms

AFRICA	Asbestos Fibre Regular Information Counting Arrangement
ARC	Asbestosis Research Council
ART	Advanced REACH Tool
BC	British Coal
BSMs	Benzene soluble materials
BSC	British Steel Corporation
BSI	British Standards Institution
CAFE	Clean Air for Europe programme
CBA	Cost benefit analysis
CBE	Commander of the Most Excellent Order of the British Empire
CEFIC	Conseil Européen des Fédérations de l'Industrie Chimique (now European Chemical Industry Council)
CEH	Centre for Ecology and Hydrology
CIEHF	Chartered Institute of Ergonomics and Human Factors
CEO	Chief Executive Officer
CNTs	Carbon nanotubes
COMEAP	Committee on the Medical Effects of Air Pollutants
CRS	Central Reference Scheme
COPD	Chronic obstructive pulmonary disease
COSHH	Control of Substances Hazardous to Health
CWP	Coal workers' pneumoconiosis
DEFRA	Department for Environment, Food and Rural Affairs

DFID	Department for International Development
DoH	Department of Health
DTI	Department of Trade and Industry
ECB	Economic Development Board
EASE	Estimation and Assessment of Substance Exposure
ECHA	European Chemicals Agency
ECSC	European Coal and Steel Community
ENPRA	Risk Assessment of Engineered NanoParticles
EDPHiS	Environmental Determinants of Public Health in Scotland
EPAQS	Expert Panel on Air Quality Standards
ERA	European Research Area
EU	European Union
EU OSHA	European Union's Occupational Safety and Health Administration (European Agency for Safety and Health at Work)
FEV	Forced expiratory volume
FRS	Fellow of the Royal Society
FVC	Forced vital capacity
GMOs	Genetically modified organisms
HEALS	Health and Environment-wide Associations Based on Large Population Surveys
HEIMTSA	Health and Environment Integrated Methodology and Toolbox for Scenario Assessment
HIA	Health impact assessment
HSL	Health and Safety Laboratory
HSE	Health and Safety Executive
ICI	Imperial Chemical Industries
ICL	Imperial College London
IEHIAS	Integrated Environmental Health Impact Assessment
IER	Institut für Energiewirtschaft und Rationelle -Universität Stuttgart (Institute for Energy Economics and Rational use of Energy – University of Stuttgart)

INSERM	Institut National de la Santé et de la Recherche Médicale (French National Institute of Health and Medical Research)
INRS	Institut National de la Recherche Scientifique (National Institute of Scientific Research)
ILO	International Labour Organization
INTARESE	Integrated Assessment of Health Risk of Environmental Stressors in Europe
IOM	Institute of Occupational Medicine
ION	Institute of Nanotechnology
IST	Institut Universitaire Romand de Santé au Travail (Institute for Health at Work)
KTL	Kansanterveyslaitos (National Public Health Institute of Finland)
MAP	Manchester Asbestos Program
MBA	Master of Business Administration
MNT	Micro and nanotechnology
MRC	Medical Research Council
MRDE	Mining Research and Development
MRE	Mines Research Establishment
NAMAS	National Measurement Accreditation Service
NCB	National Coal Board
NILU	Norsk institutt for luftforskning (Norwegian Institute for Air Research)
NIOSH	National Institute for Occupational Safety and Health
NPL	National Physical Laboratory
NNI	National Nanotechnology Initiative
NTU	National Technical University
OBE	Officer of the Most Excellent Order of the British Empire
OECD	Office of Economic Cooperation and Development
OGs	Occupational groups
OPs	Organophosphate pesticides
PCOM	Phase contrast microscopy

PFR	Pneumoconiosis Field Research
PhD	Doctor of Philosophy
PMF	Progressive massive fibrosis
PUB	Public Utilities Board
PRU	Pneumoconiosis Research Unit
PVC	Polyvinyl chloride
R&D	Research and development
REACH	Registration, Evaluation, Authorisation and Restriction of Chemicals
RCF	Refractory ceramic fibre
RICE	Regular Interlaboratory Counting Exchanges
SART	Sickness Absence Recording Tool
SDGs	Sustainable Development Goals
SEM	Scanning Electron Microscope
SEPA	Scottish Environmental Protection Agency
TNO	Nederlandse Organisatie voor Toegepast Natuurwetenschappelijk Onderzoek (Netherlands Organisation for Applied Scientific Research)
TSB	Technology Strategy Board
ULD	Upper limb disorder
UKAS	United Kingdom Accreditation Service
US EPA	United States Environmental Protection Agency
WHO	World Health Organization

Index

A

C

D

I

J

K

L

P

Q

R

T

U

V

W

Y

Z